# THE INDUSTRIAL ARCHAEOLOGY
# OF NORTH-EAST ENGLAND

## VOLUME ONE

# THE INDUSTRIAL ARCHAEOLOGY OF THE BRITISH ISLES

## Series Editor: E. R. R. GREEN

*Cornwall*, by A. C. Todd and Peter Laws
*Derbyshire*, by Frank Nixon
*The East Midlands*, by David M. Smith
*Galloway*, by Ian Donnachie
*Hertfordshire*, by W. Branch Johnson
*Isle of Man*, by T. A. Bawden, L. S. Garrad,
J. K. Qualtrough and J. W. Scatchard
*The Lake Counties*, by J. D. Marshall and M. Davies-Shiel
*Lancashire*, by Owen Ashmore
*Peak District*, by Helen Harris
*Scotland*, by John Butt
*Southern England* (second edition, revised), by Kenneth Hudson

### ASSOCIATED VOLUMES

*The Bristol Region*, by R. A. Buchanan and Neil Cossons
*Dartmoor*, by Helen Harris
*Gloucestershire Woollen Mills*, by Jennifer Tann
*Stone Blocks and Iron Rails*, by Bertram Baxter
*The Tamar Valley* (third impression, revised), by Frank Booker
*Techniques of Industrial Archaeology*, by J. P. M. Pannell
(second edition, revised by J. Kenneth Major)

### OTHER INDUSTRIAL HISTORY

*Brindley at Wet Earth Colliery*, by A. G. Banks and R. B. Schofield
*Bristol Brass*, by Joan Day
*The British Iron and Steel Industry*, by W. K. V. Gale
*The Early Factory Masters*, by Stanley D. Chapman
*The Engineering Industry of the North of Ireland*, by W. E. Coe
*A History of the Scottish Coal Industry, Vol I 1700–1815*,
by Baron F. Duckham
*The History of Water Power in Ulster*, by H. D. Gribbon

All these books are in uniform format

*The Industrial Archaeology of*

# NORTH-EAST ENGLAND

*(The Counties of Northumberland and Durham and the
Cleveland District of Yorkshire)*

VOLUME ONE

FRANK ATKINSON

For Liz,
with very best wishes,

DAVID & CHARLES
NEWTON ABBOT   LONDON
NORTH POMFRET (VT)   VANCOUVER

0 7153 5911 8

Set in 11 on 13pt Imprint and printed in Great
Britain by Latimer Trend & Company Ltd
Plymouth for David & Charles (Holdings)
Limited South Devon House Newton Abbot
Devon

Published in the United States of America by
David & Charles Inc North Pomfret Vermont
05053 USA

Published in Canada by Douglas David &
Charles Limited 3645 McKechnie Drive
West Vancouver BC

# Contents

# List of Illustrations

## IN TEXT

I know not where to seek, even in this busy country, a spot or district in which we perceive so extraordinary and multifarious a combination of the various great branches of mining, manufacturing, trading and shipbuilding industry, and I greatly doubt whether the like can be shown, not only within the limits of this land, but upon the whole surface of the globe.

Rt Hon W. E. Gladstone, 1862 (when, as Chancellor of the Exchequer, he visited Newcastle upon Tyne)

CHAPTER ONE

# *The North East*

## A GLANCE AT ITS HISTORY

SINCE late medieval times coal has been worked along the Tyne basin mostly for export by sea, and this single commodity, at first worked near the riverside and subsequently further and further from the river, has resulted in a wide range of products and structures, many peculiar to the North East. Transport of coal to the river from mines far inland necessitated miles of wagonways of ever-increasing complexity and these evolved in the nineteenth century from horse-power to steam haulage (both stationary and locomotive). Staithes, shoots, spouts and drops developed for the transference of coal from wagon to boat. Boat-building grew up on the riverside. The Newcastle 'keel', a small vessel manned by four keelmen, transhipped coal from the staithes to the larger sea-going colliers. (A man who actually mines the coal in this coalfield was until recently known as a pitman and the boats were colliers, whereas elsewhere in the country the man is referred to as a collier or a miner.) The colliers returned to the Tyne, often from the Thames, frequently with sand as ballast, and the ballast-heaps which have grown over the centuries are still a riverside feature.

Sand and coal are two necessary commodities for glassmaking; hence the development of a notable eighteenth-century glass industry. China clay was also brought back as ballast from Devon and Cornwall, making the pottery industry economical. Salt water and cheap coal resulted in the salt-making industry becoming very common in the eighteenth century around South Shields. Boat-building and repairing in the seventeenth and eighteenth centuries required large quantities of rope and assorted ironwork such as chains and anchors. Large roperies were once a feature of the Tyne basin and in

13

the late seventeenth century Ambrose Crowley, the well-known iron-master, found it worth his while to bring an entirely new industry to the North East, of which traces remain in the derelict nail and chain workshops still to be seen around Winlaton.[1]

What was true of the Tyne basin was true, to a slightly lesser degree and at a somewhat later date, of the Wear basin. The tight guild structure of Newcastle restrained Sunderland for a time, but geography and economics finally triumphed. Wagonways ran down to staithes by the riverside as far upstream as Chester-le-Street by the second half of the eighteenth century (see Gibson's map of 1787, fig 3). In fact it was first to Sunderland that Ambrose Crowley brought his iron working, but labour troubles soon compelled him to go to Swalwell and Winlaton.[2]

Our view of the significance of seventeenth- and eighteenth-century north-eastern industrial development was shared by its contemporaries. In the second half of the seventeenth century London's coal supply from the Tyne was so threatened by Dutch and Dunkirk privateers that the government provided 'cruisers' to escort the coal fleet. And in every war of the next century the French projected raids on this coast. In 1762 a Dunkirk privateer put forward plans for a raid on Sunderland: with six fast-moving corsairs and 1,500 men he proposed to destroy 'the fire mills which pump water from the coal mines in the neighbourhood'. The work, he claimed, could be done in fifteen days and the resulting destruction of the coal, salt-, and glass-works would, he contended, be quite as important as the destruction of London itself.[3]

The industrial development of lower Teesside had to wait until the nineteenth century. Coal had been worked for many centuries in south-west Durham but, until the nineteenth century, coal from there was too far from navigable water to be sold in any quantity and such pits as existed were for land sale only. Because of George Stephenson's foresight a locomotive-powered railway was laid from this area to the Tees at Stockton in 1825, and so began the railway era.

The discovery, in 1850, of iron ore in the Cleveland hills to the south of the Tees stimulated the growth of the heavy iron and steel industry around Middlesbrough and the shipbuilding which followed, whilst the anhydrite underground a little further north led to the vast chemical industry around the once tiny village of Billingham.

Sir William Armstrong of Newcastle, inventor and manufacturer, wrote imaginatively in 1863 of 'how promptly the inventive faculty of man supplies the device which the circumstances of the moment require. The seeds of invention exist, as it were in the air, ready to germinate whenever suitable conditions arise.'[4] Suitable conditions seem to have arisen in the North East, for here in the nineteenth century was produced half of the country's chemicals, the larger part of its coal, iron and steel and, on somewhat later occasions, as much as 40 per cent of the world total of shipbuilding. The annual output of the top six north-east industries in 1863 was estimated as:[5]

|  | £ |
|---|---|
| Coal | 6,650,471 |
| Metal products | 3,707,941 |
| Shipbuilding | 2,275,828 |
| Engines and machinery | 1,928,600 |
| Chemicals | 1,583,220 |
| Glass and clay products | 1,066,650 |

Of the years towards the end of the century a later writer could proudly say:

Everywhere, from the dancing waters of the harbour to the ebb and flow of the throbbing city, industry, resource and expansion, coal staiths, shipyards, engine shops, dry docks, chemical works, forges, electric lighting laboratories, warehouses, merchants' offices, steamships, railway trains, without end, without number—from Shields to Scotswood, there is not its like in 13 miles of river the world over. . . . Smoke-ridden, grimy, noisy as it all is, what is it but the free expression of nineteenth century energy, the epitome of modern industrialism, the thumb-mark of toil, by which the human race is destined to work out its salvation?[6]

Every necessary factor seemed to come together at the right moment and, as a Newcastle historian put it:

All these interconnected developments, the invention of the steamship and the railway, the tapping of deeper coal seams, the discovery of Cleveland iron, the building of docks on the Durham coast, the establishment of an effective commission for improving the Tyne, and the almost simultaneous foundation of Armstrong's and Palmer's, set the stage for the swiftest and most remarkable period of industrial expansion in the whole history of the northern coalfield.[7]

One might feel, in fact, that three things made the region what it was: money, men and minerals, though it is scarcely possible to allocate precedence, for each has played a necessary part. Capital investment in the eighteenth and nineteenth centuries is a subject too involved to discuss here, for this book is only concerned with its visible remains, yet without that desire to have money make money, the mines and machinery would never have appeared. Minerals—coal, lime, iron, lead and sand—were fortunately on hand when needed and were exploited as required, whilst men of inventive or physical prowess have ever appeared within the region. The pitmen, lead miners, shipbuilders and glass blowers have for the most part gone unrecorded, though names like Parsons, Armstrong, Bolckow, Vaughan and Pattison are still honoured. All have been essential and if the region is to rid itself of its old black, though once-proud image, then at least money and men will continue necessary. The men are still here, but the money has tended to go, leaving old decayed capital assets in the form of derelict mines and outdated housing.

The reasons for such large swings of the regional economic pendulum are not easy to untangle, but are at least partly the result of dependence on two heavy industries. If economic security for a region lies in diversification, then the late-nineteenth and early-twentieth centuries saw the North East heading inevitably for disaster, losing industry after industry, till eventually too much depended on coal mining and shipbuilding.

At the beginning of the nineteenth century, County Durham, for example, had a world-wide reputation for pottery, glass, carpets, worsteds, linen, leather, mustard and nails. Now, for all practical purposes, these industries are extinct. The reasons for this loss are

Page 17 (right)
*Haswell Colliery pumping-engine house. This early nineteenth-century stone structure is being preserved as a feature in the landscape*

(left) *Beamish Colliery winding engine (1855). The only remaining complete vertical winding engine in the region, with wooden headstock, this is scheduled for re-erection in the Regional Open Air Museum*

Page 18 (left) Tyne
Dock from the air, 1968.
Only one staithe remains
in use (compare with
plan on p 122, drawn in
the early 1930s);
(right) Seaham Harbour
coal drop. Chaldron
wagons of coal were
lowered to the boats by
this mid-nineteenth-
century 'drop'. It is now
dismantled and stored for
eventual use in the
Regional Open Air
Museum

various and not always easily discerned. The mustard trade was killed by competition from an article said to have less flavour, but selling at a lower price. Bad management may partly account for the loss of the potteries, though the temptation to sell out, when trade was not flourishing, to adjoining shipyards who badly needed space for expansion, may be part of the answer.[8]

The loss of the worsted industry was partly if not wholly due to the geographical positions of Durham, Darlington and Barnard Castle, for the centralisation of the wool industry in the West Riding drew trade away from wider-spread manufactories, whilst the cheap carpets produced at Barnard Castle were replaced in cottage homes by yet cheaper linoleum.

Nails, once extensively manufactured, are no longer produced and the trade was taken to Staffordshire a century or so ago, on account of cheaper production there partly due to the use of women workers. It is a curious fact that, except in the textile industries, women have not been greatly employed in the North East. Even the coal industry, which in Scotland and Lancashire leaned heavily on women, never used them to any notable extent in this region. This, one imagines, was not on account of respect for the fairer sex, and indeed the employment of women may be said to indicate some sort of equality. Rather, it would seem to follow a belief that a woman's place is in the home, to care for her man when he returns.

Whereas the withering away of so many and varied industries was, over the past century allowed to go on unremarked, the planner of today deliberately tries to reverse the process. Diversification of industry is currently being consciously sought as an alternative to the two heavy industries of recent years but, as can now be seen, this is not an innovation but a return to a position once naturally operating.

Thus the North East, once a busy, dirty and untidy mass of heavy industry is now reduced in busyness and striving hard to rid itself of dirt and untidyness. It is the early important and large-scale developments followed by relative industrial poverty and consequent lack of continued development that give the area its fascination to the

B

industrial archaeologist. Here one can find hidden in the undergrowth an eighteenth-century steel furnace.[9] A shrivelled coal port may still have mid-nineteenth-century port facilities rusting by its dockside and eighteenth- and nineteenth-century wagonways can still be traced for miles.[10] But things are changing socially and economically, and the desire for tidyness and a 'new image' is sweeping away derelict collieries almost daily and replacing old industrial sites with new factories.

Many items described in this book can still be found elsewhere in England but some of those relating to coal, iron, lead and rail transport (both horse and steam) are of special interest. One hopes that a selection of these can be firmly preserved and not merely allowed to remain standing by default.[11] The North East has held an important place in the heavy industrial development of this country and it would be unfortunate if all trace were to be destroyed in an effort to forget the unhappy immediate past.

### GEOLOGICAL STRUCTURE[12]

Before looking at the industrial remains of the region it will help if we take a glance at the underlying rocks and where and how they lie, for from these have come the materials of industry, and a map showing the locations of past industries is frequently a reflection of the underlying geology.

Geological history, like the much shorter history of mankind, is a series of turmoils and peaceful eras: the periods of 'turmoil' being mountain-building earth movements when the rocks were pushed, bent, twisted and broken, and the 'peaceful eras' being those lengthy times when sand, mud and other materials were brought down from the hills and deposited in the seas, to be compressed eventually themselves into new rocks, or those periods when even less detritus was washed down and in clear shallow waters great thicknesses of limestone were laid down.

Throughout a large part of the geological history of North-East

England there have been two large blocks which have remained fairly stable and relatively unaffected, though the rocks around have been bent and faulted or broken. To the north the Cheviot Hills are the outward sign of a huge volcanic mass which has existed for some 350 million years, since Devonian times. This area is mostly built up of lavas with a mass of later granite at its centre. Nearer the south of our region the other firm area is known to geologists as the Alston Block. This was already a rigid area 320 million years ago when the Coal Measures began to be formed. Between these two stable areas a great thickness of rock was deposited, to a maximum depth of several thousand feet, during the 80 or so million years of the Carboniferous period.

The Carboniferous period, so called because during this long time-span a great many coal seams were laid down, is well-represented in our region, though sediments of different kinds were being laid down over different parts of the region at the same time, and at certain times not all the region was under water. The oldest sediments were being laid down in Northumberland in lagoons which communicated with the open sea perhaps in the vicinity of the present Solway Firth, whilst the Alston region and most of Cumberland was still above the sea. Later this latter area sank and sedimentation proceeded across the whole area until all the rocks of the Coal Measures had been deposited.

Anyone familiar with the southern Pennines of Derbyshire and Yorkshire will know of the three main divisions of the Carboniferous period found there: Limestone, Millstone Grit and Coal Measures. In the North East, however, this standard sub-division cannot so easily be made. The oldest Carboniferous rocks lie around the Cheviot mass of lavas in successive layers: the oldest and lowest, which is nearest the Cheviot massif, is known as the Cementstone Group and is made up of sandstones, grey shales and rather impure limestones. Lying above these, and also dipping in a general south-east direction is the Fell Sandstone. This is a series of massive sandstones up to 1,000ft in thickness which gives rise to bold escarpments in the Border country. These rocks are generally too coarse and soft for building purposes, but some parts are fine-grained and yield a freestone of high quality as, for example, at Doddington Quarries north-east of Wooler.

The next rocks to be deposited were the Scremerston Coal Group: rather like the Cementstone Series, with shales and impure limestones, but this time accompanied by coal seams. At Berwick this group attains a maximum thickness of 1,000ft and has at least ten workable coal seams, some over 6ft thick. To the south the coal diminishes and at Alnwick there are only four thin seams, though further south-west in the Redesdale and North Tyne valleys is the Plashetts Coal, a 6ft seam which is no longer worked.

None of the rocks so far described occur south of the Tyne, but the next group of rocks, which includes limestones, is continuous over wide areas of Durham and Northumberland. In particular the main limestone measures are to be found in west Durham, providing the upper reaches of Weardale and Teesdale. Here the limestones have been frequently faulted and were once rich with lead veins now largely extracted, and other minerals. This region, the north Pennine massif or Alston Block already mentioned, is defined to the north by the Stublick fault, to the west by the Pennine fault and to the south by the Lunedale and Butterknowle faults. Roughly north-south across its centre runs the Burtreeford fault. It is worth noting that the Stublick fault has resulted in small 'pockets' of coalfield being brought to the surface to the south and east of Hexham, the tiny Planmellor and Stublick coalfields for example, and these have played their part in the siting of eighteenth-century lead smelt-mills.

Above the limestones come a series of measures which are the equivalent of the thick Millstone Grits of the central Pennines, but which are here only a few hundred feet thick and made up of shales and grits.

Finally, above all these, were deposited the Coal Measures up to 1,800ft thick. On the whole, shales and mudstones predominate, though there are many sandstones. Coal itself, though the most valuable constituent, averages probably less than 5 per cent of the Coal Measures. Some of the other materials which are, or have been, of industrial importance are:

*iron-ore:* some of the shales contain nodules or bands of clay-ironstone which were at one time mined as an iron ore.

*sandstones* which provide building stones and grindstones, some having special characteristics. The 'Newcastle Grindstone' has been worked south of Newcastle in beds totalling 120ft thick.

*ganister,* a fine-grained sandstone, of extremely high silica purity, which has furnished refractory material for furnace linings: for example the Tow Law Ganister.

*fireclays* used in the manufacture of firebricks and sanitary ware.

*shales and mudstones,* used for the manufacture of building bricks.

The workable coal seams, which give the general name Coal Measures to 1,800ft of rocks, number some fifteen to twenty. They occur mostly in the lower 900ft and vary in thickness from 3 to 6ft. Geologists have not succeeded in proving any single coal seam to be common to the two coalfields of Cumberland on the west and Northumberland and Durham on the east; but between the northern and southern counties of our region some correlation is possible, although the majority of seams carry a number of local and confusing names. The character of the coals varies according to their location: steam-raising and house coals predominate in Northumberland, while in Durham these change to coking coals, particularly towards the west, and gas coals to the east. South Durham has provided general-purpose coal. As is to be expected therefore, remains of early coke-ovens are chiefly found in west Durham. Most of the thicker seams throughout the coalfield are now exhausted, for production has been active since at least Elizabethan times, and present production is being concentrated to the east where considerable coal reserves exist under the North Sea.

After the conditions of deltas and swamps with luxuriant vegetation, which ultimately formed our coal seams, came a period of earth movements during which the Pennines were formed and the north-eastern coalfield was raised, gently folded and faulted.

Next a lengthy period of weathering gradually wore down the eastern uptilted coal seams and then this area sank to become an ancient 'Dead Sea'. Into this sea were deposited thick layers of sediment which we now recognise as Magnesian Limestone, a creamy, fine-textured rock which is responsible for the warm-coloured older farm and industrial buildings of east Durham and for magnificent coastal features such as Marsden Rocks, south-east of South Shields. Here also were deposited thick beds of yellow sands, now quarried around Boldon and Sherburn.

Further subsidence was followed by relatively stable conditions during which sandstones and marls were deposited. These, to the west and south-west of Middlesbrough are rarely seen at the surface, but are known from borings. They were laid down in seas enclosed by deserts, and at times these areas of water dried up and various salts were deposited, predominantly gypsum and common salt. The gypsum later became converted to anhydrite. The salt is got by brine-pumping, especially around Greatham (the home of 'Cerebos' salt) and Middlesbrough. Further inland around Billingham the salt decreases and anhydrite increases until it occurs in beds 50ft thick. This has led to the development of the modern chemical industry of the Billingham area.

Subsequent to these arid conditions, a widespread submergence resulted in marine conditions over the south-eastern part of our area. The lowest of the rocks deposited at that time, namely those south of the Tees, are largely buried under later silts brought by relatively recent river-flooding; but as one goes south-east towards the Cleveland Hills, one crosses a series of ironstones, mudstones and the like which were originally deposited in a widespread but shallow muddy sea. At that time the mature rivers were bringing not sandy material but fine mud, and in that environment some 180 million years ago, marine life abounded. The rocky coast of today, for example around Whitby, is a fine hunting-ground for ammonites and other fossil shells dating from that period.

A relatively thin, but economically very important, series of rocks

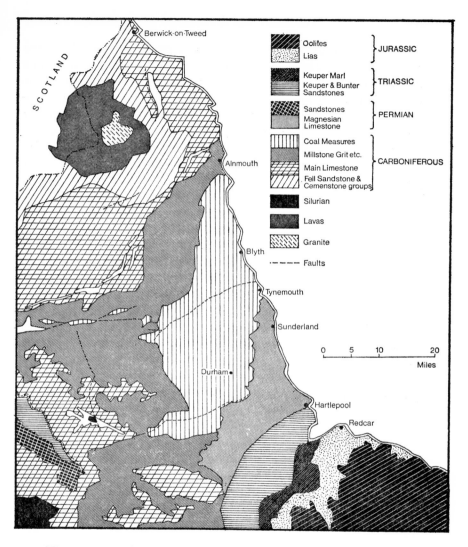

Berwick-on-Tweed

SCOTLAND

Oolites
Lias } JURASSIC

Keuper Marl
Keuper & Bunter
Sandstones } TRIASSIC

Sandstones
Magnesian
Limestone } PERMIAN

Coal Measures
Millstone Grit etc.
Main Limestone
Fell Sandstone &
Cemenstone groups } CARBONIFEROUS

Silurian

Lavas

Granite

Faults

Alnmouth

Blyth

Tynemouth

Sunderland

0    5    10        20
Miles

Durham

Hartlepool

Redcar

1   The structure of the North East: a simplified geological map. Most of the rocks shown here are not visible at the very surface, for in some areas they are covered by drift left behind by glaciers, elsewhere by alluvium from river-flooding, and almost everywhere by soil

can be traced round the lower slopes of the Cleveland Hills: the Ironstone Series. This has been one of the richest sources of bedded iron ore in England. It comprises a number of individual ironstone seams all of which are thicker around Eston Moor, thinning to the south. The main seam alone at Eston is over 10ft thick, and altogether there has been more than 15ft of workable ironstone in that area.

These beds on the Eston Hills were discovered in 1850 by John Vaughan, and so rich were they seen to be that within nine weeks quarrying was under way. The first blast furnace was built in Middlesbrough in 1851 and six years later there were 2,000 miners at work in the Guisborough area. Now the area has been so worked as to be no longer economic and the last mines closed only a few years ago; already the landscape is becoming rural again.

Here our geological tour of the North East ends. From the lowest Carboniferous rocks lying up against the Cheviot lavas in the north, to the rich ironstone seams in the south, these varied rocks have been responsible not only for the topography and soils, but for a range of products—coal, iron, lead, sandstone, to mention a few—which have so largely been responsible in turn for the historical and industrial developments of North-East England.

*Notes to this chapter are on p 195.*

# CHAPTER TWO

# *Coal*

## THE GROWTH AND DECLINE OF THE INDUSTRY

COAL was the making of the North East in the eighteenth and nineteenth centuries and has been its biggest tragedy in the mid-twentieth. Easily extracted from the steep banks of the river Tyne, coal has been mined there since Elizabethan times. The river gave an immediate means of shipment at a time when water was the only satisfactory method of bulk transport, for the rutted and unsurfaced land tracks were only suitable for local use or for pack ponies.

Towards the middle of the seventeenth century as the demand for fuel increased and the shortage of timber grew more acute so the Newcastle coalfield prospered, and the eventual pressures forced aside the jealously organised power of the city and permitted the Wearside expansion to follow. To the north, by the mid-eighteenth century, the coalfield had begun to be exploited for export, and the building of Seaton Sluice (1761–4) enabled that land-locked port to develop, with Blyth still further north having its own export trade.

Gradual exhaustion of the seams along the Tyne banks led to coal being worked a little distance from the river, with the consequent need for tracks down to it. As Fig 2 shows, there was a steady expansion of the worked coalfield until, by the middle of the eighteenth century, wagonways ran up to seven or eight miles from the mines to the Tyne. At first these wagonways were rough tracks but under increased and regular use they were elaborated and extended until a complex network of metal-railed routes covered the coalfield (Fig 3).

Meanwhile, mining methods were being improved: finding the coal seams by boring, sinking deeper shafts, transporting the coal from further and further underground. As the underground workings ex-

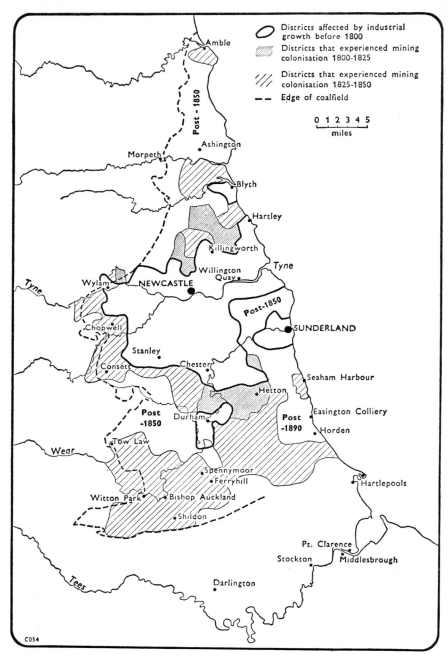

Districts affected by industrial growth before 1800

Districts that experienced mining colonisation 1800-1825

Districts that experienced mining colonisation 1825-1850

Edge of coalfield

0 1 2 3 4 5
miles

Amble

Post - 1850

Ashington

Morpeth

Blyth

Hartley

Killingworth

Willington
Quay

Tyne

Wylam

NEWCASTLE

Tyne

Post-1850

Chopwell

SUNDERLAND

Stanley

Chester

Consett

Seaham Harbour

Hetton

Easington Colliery

Durham

Post
-1850

Post
-1890

Horden

Wear

Tow Law

Spennymoor

Ferryhill

Hartlepools

Witton Park

Bishop Auckland

Shildon

Pt. Clarence

Stockton

Middlesbrough

Tees

Darlington

C054

2   The gradual expansion of the worked coalfield. (From A. E. Smailes, *North England*, 1960)

tended so did the need for ventilation and drainage. Flooded workings were a loss to the mine owner, but explosions were more serious for the workers. So 'fiery' were some of the deeper Tyne Valley collieries that work by candlelight was quite impossible and recourse was had to phosphorus and the luminescence of rotting fish. Yet there had to be the tragedy of a major explosion (at Felling in 1812) before public pressure caused any improvement, and Humphrey Davy and George Stephenson practically simultaneously produced their safety lamps.[1]

Above ground the expanding industry began, in the very early years of the nineteenth century, to adopt more mechanisation. In 1805 the first stationary haulage engine was constructed to raise coals from the valley at Birtley near Gateshead to the heights of Black Fell, from whence the wagons ran down to the Tyne. So began a series of new rail-routes, with engines sited on hilltops, and further expansion of the coalfield became practicable. Such increase in coal shipments led to the introduction, at Urpeth in 1811, of the 'drop' (p 44) whereby a loaded coal wagon was lowered to the waiting ship, with great reduction in coal breakage.

Small coals had been a great problem for many decades. They were difficult to handle and in little demand, so the low price obtainable, combined with the duty chargeable on them, led to much being packed away underground, or burnt to waste above ground. In some instances in the early nineteenth century as much as one-third of the whole output of a colliery was so destroyed. The development of screens for the separation of very small coal was therefore only to be expected, and the great expansion of the coking industry at last provided a use for an otherwise waste material. So much so that a writer in 1848 mentioned: 'of late years a new and important trade has been opened for the small coal, in the formation of coke, for the use of locomotive engines, iron works, breweries etc. . . . So rapid has been the increase of this trade that some collieries have erected an apparatus for crushing their large coal into small, the better to effect the production of coke'.[2] The trade had turned a full circle!

It is hardly surprising that the rail locomotive was first tried out in

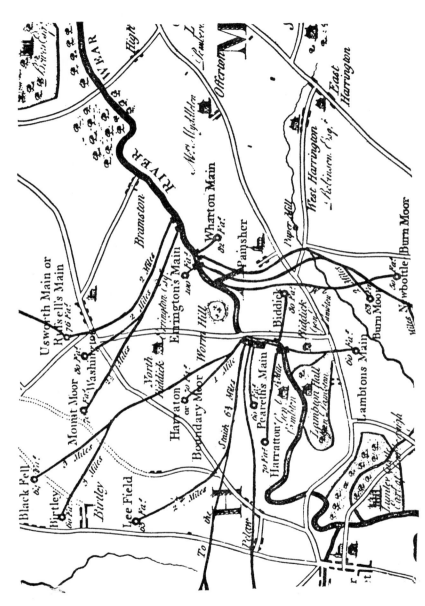

3 Part of a map by John Gibson, 1787, showing the collieries and wagonways. (The scale is approximately $\frac{3}{4}$ in to the mile)

the 'Great Northern Coalfield', for here the early years of the nineteenth century were exciting ones in the field of industrial expansion
and experiment. In this area the talents of George Stephenson,
Timothy Hackworth and others had scope for flourishing. A few
years later, iron-built colliers were being constructed on the Tyne
and the first screw steamer, the *John Bowes*, was launched at the
Jarrow Yard of Palmer, Brothers & Co Limited on 7 July 1852. The
iron shipbuilding industry and the locomotive industry were nur-
tured by the coal industry they initially served, whilst they in turn
encouraged the growth of the iron industry, and this required an ever
larger coking industry. Meanwhile the glass and pottery industries
were still thriving, brought into being on cheap small coal and cheap
raw materials brought in as ballast.

It was a period of prosperity and growth. Between 1835 and 1839
Newcastle was given its well-planned, well-designed and well-built
centre by Richard Grainger the speculator and builder and John
Dobson the architect. The nucleus of Middlesbrough was begun in
1830, and by 1851 the new town already had a population of 7,600.
Middlesbrough and Seaham Harbour share the distinction of being
the first new towns created by railways, both for the shipment of coal.
Dobson, too, was responsible for the Marquess of Londonderry's
development at Seaham Harbour: this town plan was begun shortly
after the harbour works were commenced in 1828.

And so the coalfield generally prospered throughout the century,
especially to the east where the deeper untouched seams could now
be worked by ever-improving techniques. On the western side of the
coalfield the seams were beginning to show signs of exhaustion and
less finance was available for improvement as the century drew on.
One is not surprised therefore to see, for example, that Beamish
Colliery, which was provided with an early (No 20) winding engine
by Joicey of Newcastle in 1855, continued to operate this right
through to 1961. At Ferryhill, on the other hand, the large Dean &
Chapter Colliery was sunk in 1900 and by 1965, when it closed, had
completely altered the landscape, adding an extensive modern colliery

colony to a rural 'green village' and depositing an enormous pit heap
visible for miles and covering some fifty acres.

Today the Northern coalfield is almost worked out except for the
undersea reserves, and one by one the older collieries are closing and
their sites being cleared. Gone are the days when it could be written
(1857): 'In proceeding to notice the methods of obtaining the coal,
and the general economy of a mine, we will refer to the collieries of
Northumberland and Durham, as exhibiting the most perfect
arrangements that have yet been made in this department of
mining.'[3] The region is left with derelict, mean pit villages which
have lost their *raison d'être*, with pit heaps and scarred countryside
and with unemployment. Only around Teesside has the chemical
industry come as a major replacement, founded on the anhydrite and
salt reserves and aided by a rivermouth capable of ample development.

### METHODS OF MINING[4]

One can hardly expect many visible remains of an industry largely
carried on underground and most of the items of interest to the industrial archaeologist will be surface buildings and machinery
generally concerned with the transport of the coal. Miners' tools,
however, are to be seen in several museums in the region, notably
the Museum of Science & Industry at Newcastle, at Sunderland, and
in the collections of the Regional Open Air Museum at Beamish in
County Durham. Modern large-scale surface excavations for coal are
well worth watching, for sometimes the coal seam proves to have been
previously worked and these old workings may yield occasional tools
such as wooden 'crackets' or working stools, wooden shovels and
sledges.

Before the coal seams could be exploited they had first to be discovered and, without modern geological knowledge and expertise,
boring was the only way of exploring the rocks short of the expense of
actually sinking a shaft. As long ago as 1605 boring rods were introduced to the north for exploratory work by Huntingdon Beaumont,

'an ingenious gentleman' whose family had coal mines in Leicester-shire. A century later an anonymous writer, known only by his initials 'J.C.', published a very useful little book *The Compleat Collier*[5] which included a vivid description of boring: 'Two labourers at a time . . . chop or pounce (the rods) up and down, to cut the Stone or Mineral, . . . so that finding your Rod to have cut down four or six inches, they lift up the Rods and . . . taking off the cutting Chissel, put or screw on the whimble or scoop which then takes up the cut stuff. . . .'

The rods were each several feet long, about 1½in square, with a screw at each end (one to screw into the other) and somewhat swollen at each end. The chisel-bit, about 18in long and with a 2 or 3in cutting edge, was screwed at the foot of the rods and the upper-most rod had a loop for a wooden cross-handle. Fig 4 is taken from a book *Fossil Fuel*[6] published in 1835 and shows boring in operation. K and H are rods, K being chisel-ended; M is a spanner and N an

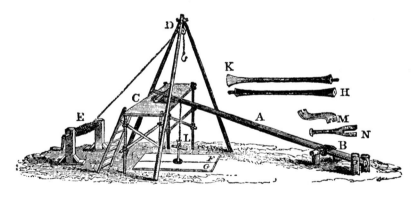

4    Rock-boring tools. (An illustration taken from *Fossil Fuel* by
John Holland, 1835)

iron fork to grip the rods below the 'swell' in order to hold the lower rods while the one above is being screwed off or on. The springy pole A imparted a springing rhythm, thus enabling the borers to lift the rods high enough to give sufficient impetus to the next blow. A set of rods not unlike this illustration recently came into the collections of the Regional Open Air Museum, and was certainly used in the early years of this century.

As late as the early years of the eighteenth century, when coal had been proved, the shaft was sunk manually and the tools of the sinker would be mattocks, gavelock (a stout iron bar for levering), a sledge hammer and wedges. Although gunpowder had been used in metal mines for a century or so, it was not used in coal mines until early in the eighteenth century. Another improvement which came into use, perhaps about 1830, was the provision of a movable iron hut, which remained in the working area as the shaft continued to be sunk. It saved loss of time occasioned by men ascending and descending, for the workers retired into it whilst the shots exploded. Such a hut, remarkably enough, still stands near the water-pumping station at New Hesledon, County Durham. It was probably used there when that shaft was sunk in 1879 and is now being preserved at the Ryhope pumping station.

The deeper mines, which were made possible by eighteenth-century improved techniques, suffered from flooding, and many were the ingenious drainage machines devised to counter the water. Tipping buckets were hauled by horses working gins (a species of windlass) and rag-and-chain pumps were worked by horses or by waterwheels. In the early years of the eighteenth century the Newcomen steam engine appeared at an opportune moment, and was welcomed by desperate mine owners. The 'Fire-Engine', as it was then called, was soon to be seen at work along the banks of the Tyne. The Newcomen engine is too well-known to be described here and it has left few remains in the North. Only two ruined pumping-engine houses still stand, one on Gateshead Fell overlooking the Tyne, the other at Haswell, County Durham. Both date from the early years of last century, and probably held Cornish engines or modified Newcomen engines. Both are apparently to be saved as historic monuments and each makes a dramatic contribution to its landscape.

Page 35 (left) *Causey Arch, a wagonway bridge of 1727. The oldest railway bridge in the world (if a wagonway bridge may be so described). It is scheduled as an Ancient Monument, and lies on the route of a footpath;* (below) *chaldron wagon at Seaham Harbour. Coal wagons of this type were once very common in the Durham and Northumberland coalfield. The last few, from Seaham Harbour, have been saved by the Regional Open Air Museum*

Page 36   (above) *Colliery housing at Hetton. Late nineteenth-century terrace houses, each of three rooms;* (below) *Hebburn Colliery in 1844. This engraving comes from T. H. Hair's* Views of the Collieries of Northumberland and Durham, *and shows a ventilating shaft on the left and screens on the right. Corves (baskets) of coal are being raised from the pit-shaft*

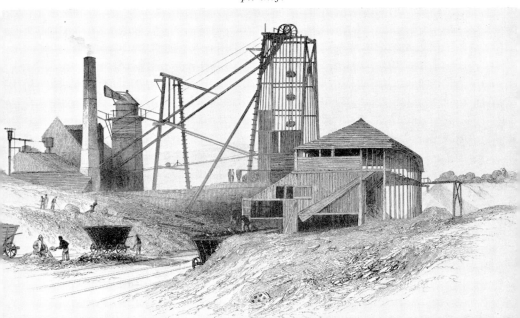

It was a pumping engine, reputedly one of the largest ever built, which caused one of the greatest pit tragedies of the North in 1862, when the beam broke and almost half of it fell down the shaft, effectively blocking it for five days. Two hundred and four men and boys perished (this number included 3 ten-year-old, 2 eleven-year-old and 11 twelve-year-old boys).[7] Slight trace of the Hester Pit, New Hartley Colliery, where this accident took place, can still be seen, for the stone walls surrounding the main shaft and an adjoining shallower shaft stand in the gardens to the rear of houses on the west side of Hester Gardens. The inscribed memorial to the tragedy is in Earsdon churchyard where most of the dead were buried. Such a tragedy served to emphasise the need for more than one shaft to each colliery and indeed a short Act of Parliament appeared before the end of 1862, making this compulsory for all new collieries.

It is difficult for us today to realise that a colliery could manage with one shaft for so many functions. Not only were men and coal wound in the shaft, and water pumped from it, but foul and fresh air was also channelled up and down it. The contemporary nomenclature is confusing, for the entire tubular hole was called a pit and this was subdivided vertically, by wooden partitions called brattices, generally into two or three shafts. One of these shafts might be occupied by the pumping mechanism, a second formed the downcast and a third the upcast shaft, for the movement of air. Ventilation was achieved in various ways. Throughout last century many collieries employed ventilation furnaces. A large fire continually burned near the foot of the shaft and the consequent rising hot air drew up with it the foul air from the mine, which had been brought to the foot of this upcast shaft by an elaborate 'coursing' or channelling of its route. The air was thus taken all the way round the workings so that no part was left unventilated and where this necessitated closure across a 'gate' or working passage, a door was hinged and a new class of worker, the trapper boy, came into being. His task was to open the door when required.

Above ground, a faintly smoking chimney took the fumes from the

c

upcast shaft and nearby a ventilator cowl swung over the downcast shaft to assist the downward passage of the air. Plate, p 36 is taken from Thomas Hair's remarkable book of engraved *Views of the Collieries of Northumberland and Durham.*[8] This plate gives a vivid idea of a Durham colliery in the 1840s, at the height of the coalfield's prosperity. The remains of an upcast ventilation tower may still be seen at South Hetton Colliery.

Mechanical ventilation began to be used in the 1880s though naturally, since such machinery has been of vital importance to the safety of the miners, any old or inefficient apparatus has invariably been rapidly replaced and little remains today. A Waddle wheel (named after its inventor) was installed at Ryhope Colliery in about 1890 and worked until 1966. This 30ft diameter sheet-metal wheel was turned at 100rpm, originally by horizontal steam engine and later by electric motor. It was open around its periphery and air was whirled away centrifugally, thus causing a drop in pressure at its centre. Here it communicated with the upcast shaft and thus provided suitable air extraction. No other example is known to remain in the region, and this example has been dismantled and is now stored by the Regional Open Air Museum at Beamish in County Durham.

TRANSPORTING THE COAL

When we come to look for visible remains of coal transportation we shall find rather more of interest to the industrial archaeologist, though even here the understandable desire to tidy up the landscape competes with the wish to maintain monuments to the history of a disappearing industry.

The central and essential feature of a colliery was, and is, the winding mechanism to the shaft. In medieval times this was a hand-turned windlass set over the shaft. In the eighteenth century it was a horse-powered 'gin' or 'whim' set either over the shaft or adjoining it; as the horse walked round it turned a drum on to which a rope from the

shaft was wound.[9] Only two machines of this general description
remain in our region; both are in County Durham and both are late
examples. One from Waterhouses Colliery is now dismantled and
stored by the Regional Open Air Museum. It served to raise pump
spears (wooden rods) from a small pumping shaft and has not been
used this century. Strictly it should be described as a 'crab'. A very
similar machine is illustrated by a plate in Hair's *Views of the
Collieries*. The other horse-gin is still in position at East Herrington
and again served to raise pump spears. This is a later example,
probably constructed about 1890 and the shaft, originally pumped
by steam engine, provided water for a coke-oven plant. Surprisingly,
this horse-gin was still occasionally used up to nine or ten years ago
and it can be seen at work in the National Coal Board film *Nine
Centuries of Coal*.

The Northern coalfield so prospered in the eighteenth and nineteenth centuries that one would hardly expect to find a coal-winding
gin left. When, however, one looks for early steam-winders there is
just a little more hope. There is certainly one such machine preserved:
that of Beamish No 2 pit (p 17). This, built in 1855, worked until
1961, though in its last years it served only to wind men for it was not
fast enough or powerful enough to wind coal. Its headstock, with
pulleys, stands over the now blocked shaft; probably the last wooden
headstock in the coalfield. It is destined for preservation in the
Regional Open Air Museum.

The vertical winding engine, of which this is a good example, was
designed in 1800 by a Newcastle upon Tyne man, Phineas Crowther.[10]
His engines proved dependable and were used in coalfields throughout
the country. They were particularly popular in the Northern coalfield
and the tall narrow buildings which typically housed them became a
feature of the landscape. Now they have almost all gone, though as
recently as 1955 there were at least fourteen of these engines at work
in County Durham. The last, a late and much-modified large example, ceased work at Wheatley Hill Colliery in 1968. The only other
examples are those of Beamish, described above, and the Isabella

engine at Elemore Colliery, Hetton-le-Hole. This latter was probably constructed about 1826, but has been somewhat modified.

It seems that at least some of the Durham coal owners had begun to lose their advanced mode of thinking by the 1880s, for this would account for Wheatley Hill Colliery being given an engine whose prototype was eighty years old. Other collieries were more advanced, and horizontal steam winding engines still exist which were being installed at about the same time, for example at Whitburn and Washington. Horizontal steam winding engines could, until recently, be seen at Shotton and Thornley Collieries.

Other buildings and equipment adjoining the mine shaft were the 'screens' for sieving the coal; the washer for cleaning the coal, which came into use towards the end of the last century; ancillary buildings for lamp-storage, horses, wagons; loco-sheds; engineering shops, etc. No proper survey has been made of these classes of buildings and one can only mention Springwell Colliery as having a square layout for its workshops, which probably once typified such buildings.[11]

From the screens, in the nineteenth century, coal was shot into rail wagons which were another typical feature of the Northern coalfield, for these chaldron wagons or 'black wagons' were direct descendants of the eighteenth-century horse-drawn wagons in both shape, size and construction. Their tapering sides, small dimensions and bottom-discharging doors were derived from those small wagons which had already been in use for a century or more and were themselves probably based on agricultural carts.[12] The last of these wagons continued in use until the 1950s and the very last few examples, at Seaham Harbour, have been preserved for use in the colliery layout now being prepared at the Regional Open Air Museum.

The colliery wagonways which developed early in the eighteenth century and rapidly extended over the coalfield, were the routes along which horses drew their small wagon loads of coal to the riverside. As pits were sunk further and further from the river these wagonways became increasingly difficult to construct. One of the best-known, the Tanfield way, County Durham, was begun in the 1720s and necessitated a large earth embankment and a magnificent stone arched bridge over a small river. The Causey Arch, or Tanfield Arch, was constructed in 1727 as a single span of 105ft.

Other wagonways can be traced both north and south of the Tyne and the Wear, and searching for their routes can be an enthralling pastime. Some of the later ones are now being preserved as footpaths, for which purpose they serve admirably. Gibson's map of the coal-field, published in 1787, is roughly to the scale of 1in to the mile and is essential in tracing these old horse routes (Fig 3). Along several of these seventeenth- and eighteenth-century wagonways quite sizeable earthworks are still visible, good examples being at Chopwell, Ryton and Whickham.

Soon after the commencement of the nineteenth century, stationary steam haulage-engines came into use. Sited at the top of a hill one of these engines would wind up a 'set' of perhaps half a dozen loaded wagons from the colliery below. The beam engine drove a large gear which engaged a gear on a vertically-placed drum and on to this the haulage rope was wound. As the set of loaded wagons approached the hill-top it came over 'the hump'—a slight rise in the track which prevented the set accidentally running backwards down the hill after it had been disconnected from the haulage rope. Although practice varied from site to site, it was not unusual for the loaded set then to be run down the other hillside to the docks on a self-acting incline. A large horizontal pulleyed brake-wheel, just below rail level, permitted the loaded set to haul an empty set back to the incline head. This returned empty set was then despatched to the colliery by putting the haulage engine into reverse.

Haulage engines and self-acting inclines were once a common sight in the Northern coalfield but, like its other nineteenth-century features they have practically all gone out of use, and the last steam haulage-engine in County Durham, at Warden Law (south of Sunderland) went out of use in 1960. This engine, built by Murrays of Chester-le-Street in 1836, had replaced one of 1823 by Stephenson, this latter having proved rather underpowered. The Warden

Law engine was taken out in 1963 when its site was required for quarrying, and is now preserved for eventual incorporation in the Regional Open Air Museum. The last steam haulage-engine in Northumberland, at North Walbottle, ceased working early in 1968 and is now scrapped. The map showing all these inclines and haulage lines has yet to be drawn, though a few of the better-known routes have been fairly well recorded.

One might expect that a prosperous and expanding coalfield would continue to seek new ideas in the mechanisation of transport and sure enough, in 1805, a locomotive to Trevithick's design was built at Gateshead and intended for use on the Wylam wagonway. It proved too heavy however, and was never used. A Blenkinsop/Murray locomotive was brought up to the Kenton & Coxlodge tramway for a short time in 1812. This was rack-driven and never very successful. Another locomotive pioneer of the North was William Chapman of Durham, and his machine was tried out on the Lambton wagonway in 1815, with fair success. At this juncture the Wylam wagonway comes back into the picture, for in 1813 William Hedley, viewer at Wylam Colliery, carried out various experiments and eventually constructed the celebrated *Wylam Dilly*. In Hedley's workshop the foreman blacksmith was Timothy Hackworth who eventually had his own works at Shildon, County Durham.

We can thus see that George Stephenson, self-taught mines engineer, had opportunities to observe several locomotives at work and eventually, as engineer to the powerful 'Grand Allies', he was ordered to supervise the construction of a locomotive for the Killingworth wagonway. The result was the *Blucher* of 1814 and its success led to further work. In 1822 he constructed a locomotive for Hetton Colliery. It worked in and around the colliery, is shown in one of Hair's engravings, and is now preserved in the National Transport Collection, York. It was from this colliery that the Warden Law haulage line ran to Sunderland Dock. As a result of these successes Stephenson was able to convince Edward Pease that the line being planned to run to Stockton should be operated by steam locomotives and thus the well-known Stockton & Darlington Railway was opened in 1825 by Stephenson's *Locomotion* drawing a heavy load of coal and passenger wagons.

With hindsight we can now see how the confidence and ambition of the coal owners and engineers encouraged innovation: success led to further success.

At the dockside, due to the topography of the North East, coal wagons usually arrived some 20 to 40ft above water level. The staithes where the wagons stood or from which they were unloaded, changed their function over the centuries. In the seventeenth and eighteenth centuries they had been primarily for storage, since it was slow work bringing coal down by horse wagon, and the boats had to be loaded quickly if they were to make the tide. Hence stocks of coal were piled at the staithes, which were roofed over and quite extensive. In the nineteenth century, as steam haulage and locomotives speeded the traffic, storage became less urgent but improvements in the speed of discharge into the boats became necessary. Chutes were not an answer at that time as coal was still handled in large pieces and breakage and consequent wastage was avoided wherever possible.

The answer lay in lowering each loaded truck to the boat-deck so that when its bottom door was knocked open the coal fell into the ship's hold with a minimum of breakage. The first such machine, called a 'drop', was built on the Tyne at Urpeth in 1811 and its success was such that soon most staithes east of the bridge had them installed, and they were to be seen also at Sunderland. Thomas Hair, in his *Views of the Collieries*, includes a fine illustration of these coal drops at Sunderland. When Seaham Harbour was built it too was provided with drops and it was one of these latter, probably dating from about 1850, which has now been dismantled and stored for the Regional Open Air Museum. It is the very last example of this so-typical feature of the coalfield (Fig 5).[13]

Coal drops finally went out of use early in the present century and coal 'spouts' replaced them as speed became more necessary and the need for large coals decreased. The timber coal staithes of around

1900 are themselves now largely out of use. A few remain at Blyth and Amble, and a modernised set continues to be operated at Seaham

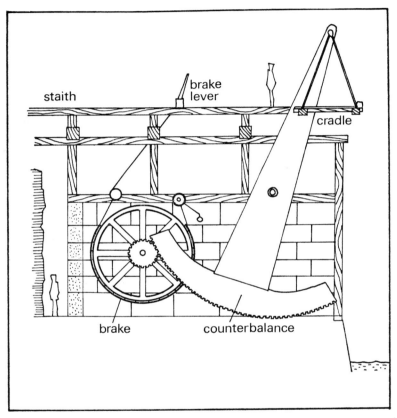

5  Mid-nineteenth-century coal drop at Seaham Harbour. The only known remaining example; these were once common on the North-East Coast (see Plate, p 18)

Harbour, whilst the foundations of several can still be observed along the Tyne. One of the most dramatic features on the Tyne is a series of archways known as Tyne Dock Arches over the South Shields to

Jarrow road (A185) and until a few years ago these carried several wagonways to a large group of staithes at Tyne Dock, where the timber foundations are still visible.

To carry the coal-haulage story to its conclusion one must mention the boats which exported the coal. Keels, or small boats carrying 21 tons of coal (8 Newcastle chaldrons), were manned three at a large oar and one at a smaller one for steerage (Fig 6). These little boats are first heard of on the Tyne in the fourteenth century and went out of use in the 1800s, finally ousted by the coal drops which, when con-

6   A Newcastle keel. (This illustration is taken from the frontispiece of *Fossil Fuel* by John Holland, 1835)

structed well down-river, could discharge directly into sea-going colliers. The keels had carried the coals from the up-river staithes down to the colliers and the coal was transferred from one to the other by hand. As mentioned earlier, iron-built colliers came into service in the middle of last century, though wooden sailing vessels are commonly to be seen on photographs of the riverside in the very early 1900s, alongside the drops. It is unfortunate that no keel or early collier has been preserved on the Tyne or Wear, though it is just possible that a wreck may one day be recognised in sufficiently good condition to justify a rescue action.

### COKING AND BY-PRODUCTS[14]

Coke is the carbonaceous deposit left after coal has been heated in an enclosed space. It was known in the thirteenth century that the residue left on a smith's hearth after heating lump coal had special properties. It was not only free from offensive smoke but it reacted less with hot iron, thereby permitting the smith to work on wrought iron without it becoming hardened. Charcoal, on the other hand, reacted with hot iron, carbonising it to form steel which was much harder to work.

Although the smith only produced small quantities of 'coaks' as they were called, a similar result was obtained by building a heap of coal, covering it with straw or hay and damp loam, and allowing this to smoulder for a day or two. This process, not unlike the charcoal burner's heap, could not be successfully used with northern coal since this swelled on heating and blocked up all the air spaces.

This is probably the explanation for stone-built ovens being first constructed in the North, in the mid-eighteenth century. These, only partially filled with coal, were nevertheless sufficiently sealed off from the atmosphere to permit smouldering without burning and at the same time to allow for the swelling of the coal. In 1765 when the French investigator Gabriel Jars visited the North he observed, near Newcastle, nine 'beehive ovens' in three batteries of three, each about 10ft in diameter. These ovens, not unlike upturned pudding basins, were of course named after the beehives of this shape then in use. Only a little under 200 years later, in 1958, the last set of beehive ovens to operate in this country was shut down near Rowlands Gill. Four of these ovens have been left on site and are preserved by the National Coal Board. The North East can thus reasonably claim to have been both the first and the last to operate such coking ovens.

Remains of beehive ovens can be traced up the western half of County Durham, for this area held coal most suitable for coking. Although beehive ovens were modified in several respects during the second half of the nineteenth century they changed relatively little externally, apart from an increase in the number of ovens to a battery. In later years they were constructed in large batteries, charged from above by small bottom-discharging hand-pushed wagons and the coke was drawn by hand on to a wide stone-built 'bench'. Sometimes it was quenched, or cooled, by water on the bench; sometimes it was quenched within the oven before drawing. The coke was then shovelled into rail wagons on a track parallel to the bench and at a lower level. These varying levels and the ovens themselves can still be traced on several sites; two good examples being at Butterknowle and East Hedleyhope.

The internal structure of beehive ovens changed during the second half of the nineteenth century in two important respects: waste heat from the process was used to heat under the floor of the oven and so speed the coking process (introduced around 1860); and the by-products of the coking process were eventually collected from the ovens and recovered instead of passing as waste into the atmosphere.

It was, however, the introduction of the vertical (or rectangular) oven, externally heated by flues, which made by-product recovery worthwhile and the first battery of such ovens in Great Britain was erected by Messrs Pease & Partners at Pease's West Colliery at Crook, County Durham in 1882. This was a battery of twenty-five Simon-Carves ovens each 23ft long, 6ft 6in high × 19½in wide, coking a charge of 4½ tons in 60 to 72 hours. A small section of these ovens was preserved *in situ* by the National Coal Board, but the site has now been levelled and reclaimed by landscaping, and the ovens have been dismantled and are stored pending re-erection in the Regional Open Air Museum.

## Tar distillation[15]

It has been claimed that coal tar was discovered by George Dixon of County Durham who, in the early 1780s, was supplying Sunderland shipbuilders with this commodity from his Cockfield works. Dixon claimed to have arrived at his results in about 1760, whereas the first patent was not taken out until 1781 by Lord Dundonald. Whoever was first, there is no doubt that Dixon was an ingenious and inventive man. He was also among the first to realise that coal possessed potentialities for illumination but, after an explosion, he came to the conclusion that the process was too dangerous to be practicable.

Coke was the first product to be obtained on a commercial scale from the heating of coal, and coke ovens were initially constructed to produce only coke, everything else (gas, tar, etc) being looked upon as waste. Yet as early as 1792 coal gas was used as an illuminant and in 1813 the Houses of Parliament were first lit with gas. Small horizontal retorts were used to produce this gas and in this process it was the coke which was the by-product and used in part to heat the retorts. Such gas works were built in most parts of the country but they have all, with one or two notable exceptions, now ceased to operate and been dismantled.

In the process of cooling the gas, tar was obtained, and this was regarded as an embarrassing nuisance, giving rise to difficulties in its disposal. One might draw a comparison with today's problem of nuclear waste from nuclear power stations; the difference however is emphasised when one learns that at one time the gas companies paid people to take the tar away. Eventually tar became a prized product, with the discovery that a range of useful chemicals could be produced from it (Perkins' discovery of the first aniline dye in 1856 was a forerunner). The tar-distilling industry then came into being.

Thomas Ness, a former railway clerk, began distilling tar in 1870 in two stills at Black Banks near Darlington, the tar being obtained from Darlington gas works and transported by horse and cart in 'rum puncheons'. The activity was converted into a limited company in 1903 and joint arrangements were made with a number of colliery companies for the operation of tar plants situated at coke ovens. In addition to the original Black Banks plant, tar distilleries were in operation at Blaydon (1905), Norwood (1915), Stella Gill and Brancepeth (1921), all later operated by Thomas Ness Ltd.

Meanwhile the introduction of the by-product coke oven, described above, increased the quantities of tar available and many of the coking plants built from 1900 onwards had tar-distillation plants. Of the 35 coking plants operating in County Durham in the 1920s, 14 had plants for distilling tar attached.

The only tar-distillation plants now in operation in the North East are those of Dorman Long on Teesside, and Thomas Ness at Blaydon, operated by the National Coal Board.

## MINERS' HOUSING

If little has been recorded about the machinery of the coalfield, less has been noted about the miners' housing. As one travels around the region, stone-built terraces begin to take on characteristics which seem different from other coalfields, but very little has been written qualitatively on these differences. Whether it be the eighteenth, nineteenth or early twentieth century, visitors to the region have rarely commented in detail on the workers' housing and detailed studies of the remaining terraces are only just beginning.

For the mid-nineteenth century we are indebted to a Royal Commission Report of 1841 which included some useful facts about mid-Durham housing:

> Within the last ten years collieries have been opened in very many places between the Wear and the Tees; and wherever a colliery has been opened a large village or town has been instantly built close to it, with a population almost exclusively of the colliery people, beershop people, and small shopkeepers. The houses have either been built by the colliery proprietors, or have been so by others, and let on lease to them, that they might locate their people.

The village of Coxhoe was quoted as typical, extending about a mile along both sides of the public road, with a break every ten or so houses to make a thoroughfare to the streets running off left and right. These cottages were built of stone plastered with lime, with blue-slate roofs, 'as like to one another as so many soldiers'. They had no yard in front, nor behind, and comprised two rooms and a semi-attic bedroom. The ground floor was made of clay, sand and lime. The whole expense of erecting such a cottage was £52 and it was rented for £5 a year. In some areas the houses had nearby pigsties, and there are references to little brick buildings in the back streets, designed as public ovens. The population of this village was estimated at 5,000, the workpeople of several collieries living there. Altogether there were thirty beershops in the village, and although at that time there was no Church of England church or chapel, the Wesleyans and Primitive Methodists had established their meetings and had many adherents.

Probably the older cottages were built close to the mines and most of the earlier ones seem to have followed the general lines of local agricultural workers' cottages. In the early years of last century new areas of building tended to follow the road line, such as Stone Row at Leasingthorne. This not unattractive single-storey row curves with the road and, although kitchens have been added at the rear and the fenestration altered at the front, it retains its general character.

A little later, as the Commissioners' Report indicates, houses were planned and built on a much larger scale, in terraces and streets. Jane Street and its neighbours at Hetton Downs (c1865) and Eden Terrace and its neighbours at Coundon of about the same date, are good examples of this planned development. Most houses now remaining were probably built between about 1840 and 1890, though small groups of earlier ones can still occasionally be observed.

The earlier houses were two-roomed only and sometimes the rooms were both on ground level, as at Stone Row, Leasingthorne (Fig 7) or one above the other as at Low Pittington (now demolished). In the latter variety the upper room would be little more than an attic, accommodated in the roof space and with very low side walls. What may well have been the next development (probably of the 1850s) is a very common type in which the upper room was improved by the addition of a dormer window and kitchen built at the rear under an extension of the back roofslope. Perhaps ten years later came another improvement on this general design, whereby the dormer window was made unnecessary by raising the front wall to give sufficient height for a bedroom window. Eden Terrace, Coundon, is an ex-

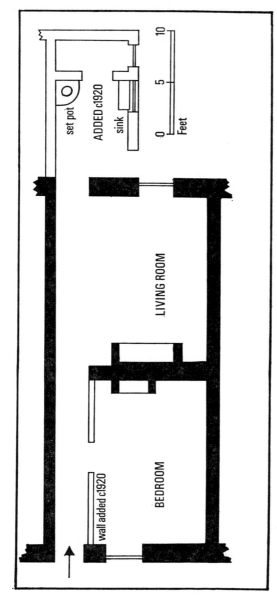

set pot

ADDED c1920

sink

BEDROOM

LIVING ROOM

wall added c1920

Feet
0    5    10

7   Plan of a miner's two-roomed cottage. A single-storey terrace house of the mid-nineteenth century: Stone Row, Leasingthorne, County Durham

ample of the dormer-windowed house, and Jane Street of the slightly later type.

Of course this brief summary cannot cover all the many house types to be found in the Northern coalfield, some quite common, others peculiar to some builder or district. There is one general type, however, which ought to be mentioned, for although very late it is being cleared very rapidly. This is the wooden-walled terrace house, which had two rooms downstairs and two upstairs. These houses were completely constructed of vertically placed timber planking, though with brick partitions and out-houses. Good examples could be seen until recently, not far from Stone Row at Leasingthorne. Here four terraces, named respectively Oak, Ash, Thorn and Yew, were built probably about 1890. Oak and Yew Terraces remained for a time, but these too have now gone. One might incidentally mention that the names of terraces and streets would make an interesting social study: cheerful or attractive names were often chosen for these serried rows.

To the rear of the houses were (and sometimes still are) clustered the pigsties and pigeon crees for the miners' spare time. Other buildings housed the communal services once provided for many of these settlements: bread ovens, wash houses and the outdoor earth closets which are now mostly converted to water-borne sewage. It may be too late to find an example of a communal bakehouse, but an interesting communal wash house and bathhouse, whilst not strictly for a mining community, was in use at Westgate in Newcastle upon Tyne until recently. Opened in 1886, it served the older housewives of the surrounding community and was greatly lamented locally when it closed in 1971.

Before venturing inside a miner's house, to see his way of life, one should draw attention to a few external structural details. The roofs of earlier cottages were covered with red pantiles, but most remaining houses have Welsh blue-slate roofs. These indicate that the houses were built (or perhaps re-roofed) after the national railway system which made it cheaper to import these slates than to buy locally-

Dukesfield lead smelt-mill flue arches. No trace of the smelt mill or its flue or chimney remains except for these two arches hidden in the wood

Lead smelt-mill flue at Stanhope. Interior view of a stone-built flue which is just a little smaller than many

Page 53

Page 54  (above) *Allenheads bouse-team. Here trucks of lead ore were tipped, as brought from the mine. Each group of miners had their ore tipped in a particular section of the store;* (below) *lead-ore crusher at Killhope, Weardale. A dramatic structure in the moorland scene, this waterpowered ore-crushing plant (about 1860) is now preserved and made available as a picnic site*

produced tiles. The house walls are built of stone, brick or wood and can again help to date their construction, whilst attached near each door may frequently still be seen the 'knocker-up' slates in small standardised cast-iron frames. On this slate the miner would chalk the time of his next shift so that the knocker-up (usually an injured miner) knew at which house to call in the early morning.

Finally, a brief glimpse inside a nineteenth-century miner's cottage will give us another view of regional characteristics. One witness to the already mentioned 1840 Royal Commissioners commented on a remarkable dissimilarity between the cottages and their furniture, which he thought to be peculiar to the Northern pitmen: whilst the houses externally were dreary and identical, he found them to contain comparatively showy and costly furniture. Typical items of furniture in the principal room were an eight-day clock, a good chest of drawers with brass handles and ornaments, reaching from floor to ceiling, and a fine four-post bedstead with a large coverlet composed of squares of printed calico. These last two were often of mahogany, and were deemed indispensable by a decent newly-married couple. They were paid for by instalments. Also mentioned in these descriptions are the dess-beds (sometimes called 'desk-beds'); there was often one in the principal room for the youngest of the family, whilst the rest of the family would be distributed in the back room and attic.

The dess-bed and a somewhat similar bed with the local name 'chiffonier' (accented on the first and penultimate syllables) were folding cupboard-beds. When closed for the day, the dess-bed took on the appearance of a sideboard often with a false pair of drawers near the top, and the chiffonier looked more like a rather squat wardrobe. They served both pride and necessity, for by day the house looked tidy and attractive and by night several beds were available for the family. They continued in common use well into this century.

Likewise gone are the nineteenth-century black-leaded cast-iron fireplaces and brass-decorated mantelpieces, while the zinc bath no longer hangs by the back door awaiting the pitman black from the mine.[16] The pithead baths revolutionised the miner's life in the

D

1930s and 1940s and the relative affluence of the 1950s and 1960s have cleared out his characteristic furniture. The houses themselves are now being demolished as the mines close and housing standards improve.

*Notes to this chapter are on p 196.*

# CHAPTER THREE

# Lead

BEFORE we can understand some of the industrial structures left by the lead industry, we need to know something of lead ore itself, how it has been formed and how and where it has been mined and worked.

In Britain, lead is never found in pure form, but is generally compounded with sulphur to form lead sulphide, commonly called galena. Unlike coal, which as we have seen was deposited in layers under water in marshy conditions, lead crystallised from a hot solution which, as it worked up from deep beneath the earth's rocky crust, dissolved silica and metallic sulphides. The solution penetrated cracks and weaknesses in the rocks and as it cooled it lined or filled these openings, depositing quartz, galena, and other minerals such as fluorspar (calcium fluoride) and barytes (barium sulphate). Naturally these did not all cool and crystallise simultaneously, and one finds pockets of one mineral or another, or crusts along the wall of the vein with one mineral deposited over the other. Moreover the rate of cooling varied from place to place and hence some very large and beautiful crystals of veinstone such as quartz or fluorspar are occasionally to be found. Additionally silver, possibly as silver sulphide, is frequently found mixed in small proportions with the galena.

Some parts of the earth's crust have suffered more earth movements and consequent cracking than others. Moreover some rock types are more brittle than others and present lines of weakness or actual openings along which the hot solutions could easily penetrate. Within our area of North-East England, the large limestone mass lying around Alston exemplifies all these conditions. It has been heavily faulted or cracked by movements, and has been deeply penetrated by mineral deposits. A circle of radius 10 miles, drawn around Wearhead, roughly indicates the area within which lead has been mined (Fig 8) although a variety of minerals has been mined further to the north and east. We also find that for various reasons the lead ore, after mining, has not always been processed within this area, but has been carried some distance away to the north or east. Within

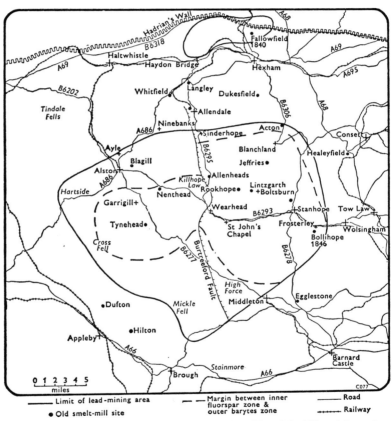

8  The lead-mining region. The lead dales: Teesdale, Weardale and Allendale, formed a compact rich ore-bearing area. (From A. E. Smailes, *North England*, 1960)

the area so delineated, lead ore and other minerals are to be found in veins, which represent cracks in the rock. The most productive veins lie roughly NE/SW though ore is sometimes found in veins running in other directions. Vein-material may vary in thickness depending upon the hardness of the surrounding rock.

It will now be clear that finding a rich source of lead ore could be a chancy affair. Even the successful identification of a vein by surface features, which in any case are usually obscured by soil and vegetation, would not guarantee a rich deposit. Yet one cannot but be impressed by the thoroughness with which all likely areas have been explored by past lead miners, who incidentally have for generations been identified as 't'owd man'. A miner following a vein might break through into a void, whence all the ore had been extracted years ago, and would say that 't'owd man' had been there before him.

Lead has been extracted from the Alston area for many centuries, and it seems not unlikely that this ore was one reason for the Roman penetration so far north. During the eighteenth century the industry grew and prospered and by the early nineteenth century enormous fortunes were being built up by local families. Lead royalties, held by the rector of Stanhope in Weardale, produced for him some £4,000 per annum around 1820. During roughly the same period the Blackett-Beaumont family was making a net annual profit of as much as £60,000 from its lead-mining activities.[1] British lead mining was at its zenith in the mid 1850s when the price of lead was £32 a ton; but the price fell to as low as £13 per ton in 1896 after the opening of lead mines in the United States, Mexico and Australia, and we find little mining continuing within our area into the present century.

When we come to look into the extraction and working of lead ore we find three main processes which have each left different archaeo-logical remains: mining, crushing and cleaning of ore, and smelting.

## MINING THE ORE

Since the lead veins are near-vertical and extend to great depths, yet may be traced along the hill-sides for several miles, they have been worked both from the surface and deep underground. No doubt the earliest workings were along the surface, for once a vein had been identified it could easily be traced and moreover this method required no capital outlay on shaft-sinking or machinery. Such worked-out veins can be traced for miles over the moorland areas of upper Teesdale, Weardale and Tynedale. New veins could be discovered and known sites cleared of soil and debris by hushing or large-scale washing and traces of this operation can also be easily found. A sod dam was constructed high on the hills, when it held sufficient water the dam was broken and the flood allowed to scour the hillside, exposing the vein and producing a spoil-heap not unlike, though on a smaller scale than, the terminal moraine of a glacier. This method was widely used, with increased size and more skilled control, until late in the nineteenth century, so that now, although hushes can be seen in many parts of the mining area, it is not easy to point to any one and say with certainty that it is a very ancient one.

Deeper penetration of the veins was made either by shaft-sinking or by driving an adit (a near-horizontal tunnel), depending upon the direction of the vein and the lie of the land. Once the vein was entered, it could be worked simultaneously upwards and downwards, its width being generally several feet. As the ore was extracted from above, false working floors could be constructed by cross-timbering and by heaping unwanted stone, known as 'stacked deads'. A section of a mine (Fig 9) shows how shafts and levels (or tunnels) were cut along and within the thickness of the vein, and how the ore was extracted from above (commonly called roof work) or from the 'sole of the mine', ie the floor of the working area. The cavity left after removal of the ore is called the stope.

Little from this mining remains accessible to the industrial archaeologist, unless he combines with that interest the skills of the miner or pot-holer. Several societies exist to explore old mines as well as natural limestone caverns, but it is a specialised and arduous business. Nevertheless, given this ability, it is possible to see deserted

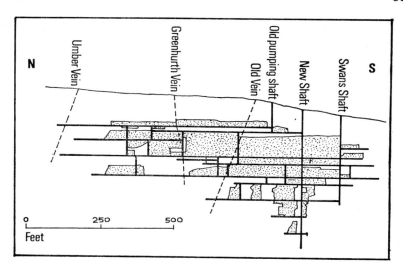

9  Longitudinal section of a lead mine. The heavy vertical lines represent shafts; the heavy horizontal lines represent levels; and the shaded areas indicate where ore has been extracted from the vein. (Based on Greenhurth Mine, County Durham, NY 783327, after K. C. Dunham, *Geology of the Northern Pennine Orefield*, 1948)

workings, occasional old tools, 'tubs' or small wheeled trucks, wooden and iron rails, drainage sumps and pumps and wooden shoots to carry ore from one level to another.

Pennine lead miners were employed on quite a different basis from northern coal miners, due to the wide variation in ore quality and quantity as compared with the relatively constant far-reaching coal seams. To understand the contracting system we cannot do better than read Westgarth Forster, a mine surveyor who wrote in 1821:

In Alston Moor, after a mine is opened and appears to be productive, the miners take a certain piece of ground, commonly called a length, in which they propose to raise Ore, for a certain time, at so much per Bing (ie. 8 cwt), according to the richness of the Mine or working. A length of ground is commonly either twelve, fifteen, or twenty fathoms, and the price of procuring the Ore, depends much upon the hardness, the expense of drawing the Stone or Ore out of the Mine, and the probable quantity of Metal that can be raised. The Miners generally take bargains, in partnerships, consisting of from two to four, six, or eight men, and the prices are from eight to fifteen, twenty, thirty, forty, or fifty shillings, per Bing; the miners always paying for Candles, Gunpowder, the expenses of drawing the Ore or Stone from the Mine, working, dressing, and preparing it, fit for the process of Smelting.[2]

## Drainage levels

Throughout the late-eighteenth and nineteenth centuries, one of the biggest problems facing the lead miner was water which flooded the lower workings. There was no danger from explosive gases and no great need for the elaborate ventilating systems found necessary in coal mines. Mines were sometimes drained by driving long 'levels' or slightly inclined tunnels from the valley-bottoms into the lead-bearing hillsides. Water drained out in this way lowered the general water-table and made the lower parts of nearby veins more accessible. Lengthy tunnels of this kind might also be cut in exploratory fashion, in the hope of striking rich veins. For example the Blackett Level, which has its portal by the riverside immediately below the church at Allendale Town, runs for $4\frac{1}{2}$ miles up the valley: it was begun in 1854 and designed to drain and explore the valley as far as Allenheads.[3] This ambitious scheme, on which £120,000 was expended, was to have been nearly 7 miles long, with four shafts reaching to the surface. Driving continued intermittently until 1903, but by this time the Allenheads mine was closed and the collapse of mining was about complete.

It had been the very rich discoveries of ore in the Allenheads area which caused the Blackett Level to be started, but although productive veins were discovered as a result of this latter work, they could not bear comparison with those of Allenheads and Coalcleugh.

Another great mine-drainage level was the Nent Force Level, nearly 5 miles long, which was driven from Alston to Nenthead during the latter part of the eighteenth and early nineteenth centuries (Fig 10). It was an outstanding mining venture, started at a time (1776) when lead mines were entering a period of great prosperity, and there can be little doubt that those who planned it realised they would not live to see it finished. It failed in one of its main objects, namely to discover major ore deposits in the unexplored strata below the river Nent, but as a drainage level it proved invaluable. If it had not been driven, many thousands of tons of lead ore would never have been raised, and a number of the mines of Alston Moor would have closed long before they were worked out. No more work was carried out on the level after 1842, and all signs of the portal have now vanished, though a photograph taken about 1900 has been reproduced.[4]

Although lead-mine ventilation was not so pressing a matter as it was with coal mines, nevertheless in a long level such as the Nent Head one, shafts had to be sunk to give a through-ventilation, and along the length of the level three shafts served this purpose (Fig 10). There is a further point of interest, for a plan of the level drawn in 1809 marks 'Water Blast Shaft' about 300ft from the portal, just above Nent Force. Water from the river was diverted down this shaft and, falling into a cistern or tub, helped to force pure air up the level and foul air out. We know that lead pipes too were used to convey air to distant parts of the working, for Thomas Sopwith, a mine surveyor, describing the area in 1833 noted that 'the present agent has made use of lead pipes . . . a great improvement on the wooden boxes formerly in use. These not only rendered the air impure, but could not be made air-tight.'

Before we leave the underground workings, mention should be made of hydraulic engines. The first such engine to be used in England was installed at Coalcleugh Mine in Northumberland in 1765 by William Westgarth. (The first hydraulic engines appear to have been used in Germany some seventeen years earlier.) Eighty years later W. G. Armstrong (later Lord Armstrong) of the then Elswick Engine Works (later Vickers-Armstrong Ltd) designed a

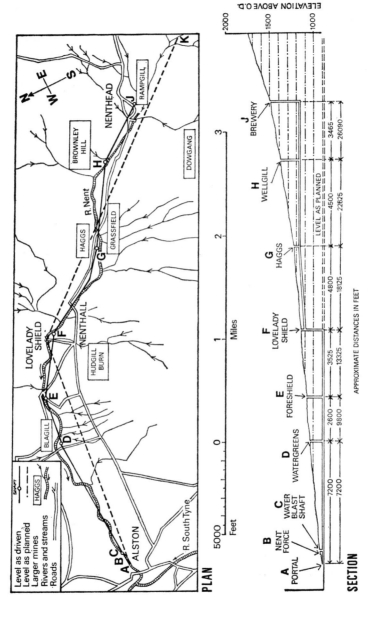

**PLAN**

Level as driven
Level as planned
Larger mines
Rivers and streams
Roads

SHAFT
HAGGS

N
W — E
S

BLAGILL
LOVELADY SHIELD
HUDGILL BURN
NENTHALL
HAGGS
R. Nent
GRASSFIELD
BROWNLEY HILL
NENTHEAD
RAMPGILL
DOWGANG

ALSTON
A B C
D
E
F
G
H
J
K

R. South Tyne

Feet
5000    0

Miles
0    1    2    3

**SECTION**

ELEVATION ABOVE O.D.

2000
1500
1000

A PORTAL
B NENT FORCE
C WATER BLAST SHAFT
D WATERGREENS
E FORESHIELD
F LOVELADY SHIELD
G HAGGS
H WELLGILL
J BREWERY

LEVEL AS PLANNED

7200    2600    3525    4800    4500    3465
7200    9800    13325   18125   22625   26090

APPROXIMATE DISTANCES IN FEET

10   Nent Force Level, 1776–1842. This extensive lead working, originally cut for exploration, drained a wide area, thus permitting further lead-ore extraction. (After P. Wilson, 'The Nent Force Level', *Trans Cumb & Westm Ant & Arch Soc.* 63, 1963).

wide variety of hydraulic engines of which several were used underground in lead mines. The Elswick works, established in 1847, specialised in the manufacture of hydraulic machinery for cranes, hoists, dock gates and the like. Thomas Sopwith, who was appointed agent to the Allendale Mines in 1845, had many friends in the scientific and engineering world of that time, among them being Michael Faraday. He also knew Armstrong, and it was probably the latter's infectious enthusiasm for hydraulic power which led to the installation of these new engines in and around Allenheads. Two were underground at Fawside Level in Allenheads mine, one at the main shaft at Gin Hill for sending men down and drawing bouse (ore), one at the saw mill, one at the dressing floors for driving the crusher, and four were installed on the shafts above the Blackett Level. The underground examples may still be in position, but all those above ground have disappeared with the exception of that at the Allenheads sawmill (see also p 154).

### CRUSHING AND CLEANING THE ORE

When ore was brought out of the mine, it was naturally mixed with various spars, veinstone, etc, and called by the miners 'bouse'. This was generally tipped in a roughly built stone hopper or 'bouse stead'. Since several groups (or partnerships) of miners would be working the mine, their loads of ore had to be kept separate and therefore a range of bouse steads was constructed, one bay to each partnership. Good examples can be seen, all built by Thomas Sopwith: at Allenheads (1857), Cowshill in Weardale (1864) and Killhope in Weardale (c1870). These bouse steads are sometimes the only significant features remaining above ground, and are often very well built. The Killhope example has rounded bays, whilst the magnificent range at Allenheads (Plate, p 54) has high stepped dividing walls and across their tops run wooden rail-supports along which the trucks of ore would be brought. (It is unfortunate that recent developments have destroyed part of this range.) Similar traces of wooden rails remain at

Killhope, where it can clearly be seen how the horse-drawn trucks were brought out of the level and run over the bouse steads, to be tipped into the appropriate bay.

The bouse was crushed and then washed in running water to separate the galena from waste materials. Some bouse was more easily crushed than others and this wide variation can be observed today, if residue from mine spoil heaps is collected and compared. For instance galena from Grove Rake Mine in Weardale can be crushed between the fingers, whereas ore from Eggleston Burn can only be broken with a hammer.

When the bouse could easily be broken, this was done by women and children using small hand-hammers on a dressing-floor. Such a hammer, known as a bucker (Fig 11), had a flat horizontal head of wrought iron with a steel face about 3 or 4in square fixed to a short

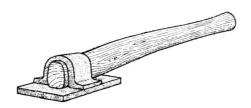

11    A bucker for crushing lead ore (see Fig 12 for method
of use)

haft; it weighed 5 or 6lb. The use of a bucker is shown in Fig 12 taken from a book of 1878.[5] When the ore was tougher and less brittle mechanical force was used.

A stamp-mill is said to have been erected by the London Lead Company in 1796, and the remains of a wood and iron stamp-mill were recently preserved from Nenthead, though there is of course no certainty that this is the 1796 example. Such mills, driven by water-wheel, comprised heavy upright wooden blocks with iron feet, which were raised and allowed to drop within guides. Stamp-mills of this description were known to German metal miners in the sixteenth century, but were only slowly accepted here.

12  Woman using a bucker to crush lead ore. (An illustration from a mid-nineteenth-century book. Ore was crushed by the bucker on an iron plate and swept to the ground by the left hand)

Only a few years after the stamp-mill was erected near Alston, another important improvement was introduced to the area. This was the crushing mill, which was so quickly adopted that by 1830 Sopwith could write: '. . . which now forms so conspicuous an object in the washing floors of large mines'. The crushing mill operated like a large coffee-mill, hard lumps of ore and stone being crushed between two rollers. In 1820 a small crusher was specially erected at Killhope in Upper Weardale because the ore there was notoriously hard, and presumably the present remains of a crushing mill are those of its larger successor probably built about 1870. The 33½ft diameter overshot wheel and buildings stand by the riverside forming a dramatic feature in this bleak area, and can clearly be seen from the main road through Weardale. (Plate, p 54.)

Nearby is the portal of Park Level which gave access to several veins. This works, owned by the Beaumont Company, crushed and dressed ore which was then transported by horse to Allenheads for smelting. This is the best remaining example of water-powered crushing plant in the North East; the whole group is now preserved, and open to the public as a picnic site.

The overshot waterwheel was powered by water brought from a complex drainage system and regulating reservoir up in the hills, by a leat which ended over a wooden structure supported on stone foundations as it approached the wheel. These stone foundations can still be seen down the hillside, although all woodwork has now gone. The wheel which, it has been calculated, provided about 40hp, turned crushing rollers and something of the heavy wooden structure which supported these can still be seen. Some idea of the actual construction and operation of this machinery can be gained by examining a drawing first published in 1821 by Westgarth Forster, who was a mining engineer in this area.[6] No other example of crushing plant exists in the northern lead field, though at Lune Head, Yorkshire, can be found a wheel-pit and indications of a mill which probably resembled the Killhope one.

After crushing, the ore was washed by various methods and a large variety of mechanical and manual pieces of equipment were involved. Most traces of these have gone, but the principal by which they operated was that, in flowing water, the heavy lead ore sank while the lighter fragments of other minerals could be carried away. To discuss ore-washing in a sentence is hardly to do justice to the considerable ingenuity which this process called forth, and the great variety of machines which are recorded in nineteenth-century text books and cyclopaedias demonstrates the mechanical skill which was applied.[7] Unfortunately none of these machines remain in our area and the industrial archaeologist can only observe a few wooden foundations which have been preserved, and recently cleared for observation, in the floor of the large building at Killhope. We must leave the ore-washing at this: the flowing water in various machines, tanks and troughs, associated with moving parts some of which were hand and some machine-powered, separated the various grades of ore until a purified galena was ready for smelting.

### SMELTING

Galena, as we have seen, is a chemical compound of lead and sulphur, ie lead sulphide (PbS). The process of extracting pure lead from this entails first roasting the crushed ore, or heating it in the presence of air, until it has all been converted to lead oxide or lead sulphate, compounds which are expressed chemically as PbO and $PbSO_4$. The resulting mixture is then mixed with more galena, air is this time restricted and heat is again applied; sulphur dioxide gas is given off and lead remains, collecting at the bottom of the furnace in a molten state. This is then run off into moulds. The breakdown of the lead compounds can be shown thus:

$$PbS + 2\,PbO \longrightarrow 3Pb + SO_2$$
and
$$PbS + PbSO_4 \longrightarrow 2Pb + 2SO_2$$

In considering the actual remains of smelt mills it may help if we try to discover when the mills were constructed and why they were built where they were.

Lead-mine output increased in the eighteenth century as demand grew and techniques improved, and to handle this increasing volume of ore more smelt mills were required. For example the Allen Mill at Allendale was opened in 1692 and the Ryton one in 1696, whilst a glance at a list of smelt mills in the North Pennines shows that 11 were opened during the first half of the eighteenth century, 4 in the second half and a further 9 in the early years of the nineteenth century.[8]

_List of Smelt Mills in North Pennines_ (Fig 13)

|   | Name of Mill | Opened | Closed | Owner |
|---|---|---|---|---|
| 1 | Feldon | 1680 | 1730 | Various & London Lead Co |
| 2 | Allen | 1692 | 1896 | Beaumonts |
| 3 | Ryton | 1696 | 1706 | London Lead Co |
| 4 | Blagill | 1704 | 1736 | London Lead Co |
| 5 | Whitfield | 1706 | 1816 | London Lead Co |
| 6 | Acton | 1710 | 1806 | London Lead Co |
| 7 | Jeffries | 1713 | 1870 | London Lead Co |
| 8 | Allenhead | pre-1725 | 1870 | Beaumonts |
| 9 | Blaydon | pre-1725 | 1870 | Beaumonts |
| 10 | Dukesfield | pre-1725 | 1834 | Beaumonts |
| 11 | Rookhope | pre-1725 | 1883 | Beaumonts |
| 12 | Lintzgarth | 1736 | 1750 | Beaumonts |
| 13 | Burtreeford | 1743 | 1750 | Beaumonts |
| 14 | Nenthead | 1746 | 1882 | London Lead Co |
| 15 | Langley | 1767 | 1887 | Greenwich Hospital |
| 16 | Gaunless | c 1770 | 1870 | Earl of Darlington |
| 17 | Egglestone High | 1771 | 1903 | London Lead Co |
| 18 | Tynehead | c 1790 | ? | J. Lowry |
| 19 | Egglestone Middle | c 1800 | 1903 | London Lead Co |
| 20 | Egglestone Low | c 1800 | 1903 | London Lead Co |
| 21 | Hilton | 1801 | 1880 | London Lead Co |
| 22 | Dufton | 1801 | 1847 | London Lead Co |
| 23 | Stanhope | 1801 | 1880 | London Lead Co |
| 24 | Cross Fell | 1804 | c 1840 | Cross Fell Mine Co |
| 25 | Healeyfield | 1805 | 1913 | Healeyfield Mines Co |
| 26 | Fallowfield | 1840 | 1847 | Walton & Cowper |
| 27 | Bollihope | 1846 | 1880 | London Lead Co |

A consideration of some of the factors which may have determined the sites of the smelt mills brings out the problem of transport which became less pressing after road building began early in the nineteenth century. For example, a description of the parish of Whitfield in 1749 states: 'The roads through the parish were trackways and the principal employment of the people was the conveyance of lead ore to the neighbouring smelt mills in sacks on the backs of ponies.' These ponies or 'Galloways' were the only means of conveyance of lead and coal over the moors. The Galloways moved in trains of ten to twenty or more in single file over the moorland tracks,

Page 71  (above) *Iron-ore calcining kilns at East Rosedale. Ore was heated in the kilns before being transported to a blast furnace for smelting;* (below) *iron-works offices of Bell Brothers at Port Clarence. A fine block designed by Philip Webb in 1876; now derelict. To the left is the blast-engine house*

Page 72 (left) *Chain-making in 1966 at Winlaton. Jack Hunter and Brian Kyle making their last chain before this hand industry ceased in the North East. The chain-shop and its contents are preserved for the Regional Open Air Museum*

(right) *a smithy dated 1822 at Ponteland*

each carrying about two hundredweights and each with an attendant man or boy. These moorland ways or 'gates' can still be traced, sometimes rather sunken and at other places, where the going was

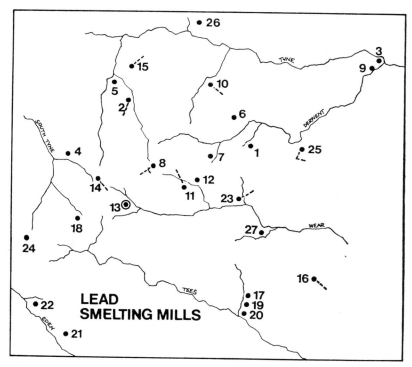

13   The North-Eastern lead smelt-mills. Most of these can still be traced on the ground and several miles of stone-built flues can be observed. The presence and approximate direction of flues is indicated by dotted lines. (For key to numbers see p 70)

soft, set with stones. A small building, possibly of about 1800, near Egglestone is still known locally as the 'saddle house' and local tradition recalls that the pack saddles of the Galloways carrying ore down to the Egglestone smelt mills were stored here. Two wooden saddles taken from this building are now preserved (Fig 14).

E

Fuel for smelting might be peat or coal; a peat house at Allenheads is the only building remaining on the smelt-mill site, but most other sites do not have buildings so easily recognisable. Coal sometimes had to be transported a fair distance and there is proof that at least one

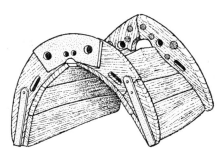

14    Wooden pack-saddle. In the Regional Open Air Museum collection, and taken from the Egglestone saddle-house, this was used to carry lead ore on the back of a Galloway—a sturdy pony

smelt mill was established (Whitfield Mill, by the London Lead Company in 1706) in order to reduce transport costs. The lease of this mill included the lease of a colliery at Coanwood, on the south border of the tiny Planmellor coalfield about 3 miles south-east of Haltwhistle. The following record of 1706 quoted from Raistrick and Jennings, *History of Lead Mining in the Pennines*, clearly shows the effect of transport costs on the decision to establish this mill:

|                                                                                      | £ | s | d |
|--------------------------------------------------------------------------------------|----|----|----|
| 5 bings of ore may yield about 1 fother of lead and may be carried to Whitfield (from Alston Moor) for: |    | 13 | 4 |
| The fother of lead carried to Ryton:                                                 |    | 13 | 4 |
|                                                                                      | 1  | 6  | 8 |
| 5 bings carried to Ryton:                                                            | 1  | 15 | 0 |
| So there will be saved carrying it to Whitfield:                                     |    | 8  | 4 |
| The coals may be dearer at Whitfield than at Ryton for smelting so much ore:         |    | 1  | 4 |
| So that a fother of lead would be cheaper at Whitfield than at Ryton by:             |    | 7  | 0 |

Langley Mill, near Langley Castle in Northumberland, was built in 1767 on a site selected with reference to the small Stublick coalfield only half a mile away, and to the main Allendale road which linked it with all parts of Alston Moor. This mill (see also p 78) rapidly achieved importance and was finally dismantled in 1887. A similar relationship between coalfield and smelt mill can be seen in the siting of many other mills; Nenthead mill used some coal from Coanwood and some from several small local mines; Egglestone and Stanhope drew their coal from mines mainly in the Millstone-Grit coals in the Bishop Auckland area.

### Smelting hearths

To come now to the hearths themselves, where the smelting process was carried out, we find a bewildering series of names and descriptions.[9] The *ore-hearth* or *blast-hearth* was a simple hearth which during the eighteenth century, became quite standardised. An early-nineteenth-century description refers to it as the Scotch furnace, 'which is generally employed in the Counties of Northumberland, Durham and Cumberland.' There is, in the library of the Literary & Philosophical Society at Newcastle upon Tyne, a manuscript of about 1795 written by James Mulcaster, Agent to the Governors of the Greenwich Hospital.[10] This vividly describes an ore-hearth smelting, with its alternate 'settings-up' of a peat and coal fire on to which part-smelted ore is put, and 'watchings' when the heated mass of bouse is drawn forwards on to the workstone at the front of the hearth, across which runs a small gutter. Molten lead drains from the mass of bouse and runs down the gutter into a sump for casting into pig-moulds. Whilst one man is dragging forward this mass of bouse, his partner is re-setting the fire with peats. The drained bouse is then lifted by both men back on to the fire and a small mass of fresh ore is placed on top 'where it undergoes a temporary roasting which fits and prepares it a little for its being brought into the most vehement part of the fire. These watchings and settings-up are generally performed once in every five minutes. . . .' Throughout the process a steady blast of air was needed, supplied generally by water-powered bellows. The chemical process described in theory on p 69 can be recognised in practice here.

The *slag-hearth* resembled the Scotch furnace or ore-hearth and was used to smelt slag remaining from other processes, particularly that used to obtain silver from lead. In place of the workstone was a shallow fore-hearth, partially filled with hot cinders, where the molten lead collected and from whence it drained into an iron pot which was kept heated by a small fire. Beyond lay a cistern or shallow tank full of water and supplied by a continual cold stream. The slag was allowed to flow out of the furnace, over the cinders in the fore-hearth and into the water, where it flew to pieces, after which it was easily washed so as to separate the small amount of remaining lead. Being more viscous than the molten lead, the slag would flow over the cinders in the fore-hearth, while allowing lead to flow from it through the cinders.

The *cupola* or *reverberatory* furnace was perfected about 1690 by Dr Edward Wright, a physician and metallurgist. He became a member of the Ryton company which was established in 1696 to smelt lead ores from Alston Moor at Ryton-on-Tyne. The reverberatory furnace differed in every way from the ore-hearth, being a horizontal furnace with a separate fire-box. Only flames and hot air were drawn over a low fire-bridge to work upon the ore in the bed of the furnace. Bellows were not needed and thus this furnace was not so dependent upon a large stream of water for power.

The furnace had two main parts: fire-box and furnace-bed. The furnace-bed was a low chamber with concave floor and slightly arched roof. There were small doors at each side through which the contents could be stirred by poker and above was a hopper or charge-hole. At the lowest point of the furnace-bed was a tapping-hole which led to an iron sumpter pot for the molten lead.

Despite their higher efficiency, cupolas were not so popular in the North as ore-hearths. The advantages of the latter were that they could use any fuel (peat, wood or coal) while the reverberatory furnace required coal. Moreover the operation could be started quickly and would produce lead soon afterwards: a small quantity of ore could be worked through at any time. So the ore-hearth was ideal for small partnerships. In reverberatory smelting much larger quantities were handled and more uniform dressing and preparation of ore was required.

The *roasting furnace* was similar to a reverberatory furnace, but had a flat bottom since the process was not carried far enough to produce lead. The roasted ore could then be more rapidly smelted on the ore- or blast-hearth and moreover was believed to produce a purer metal.

## Smelt-mill flues

One feature of the northern lead smelt-mills remains to be described—their flues. The fumes of smelt mills were highly poisonous, containing as they did not only sulphur dioxide, but quantities of lead which vapourised and emerged with the smoke.

Bishop Watson, in his *Chemical Essays* (1778), pointed out that this loss of lead was appreciable to the smelt-mill owner and he suggested the use of horizontal chimneys of sufficient length to condense the lead fumes. The London Lead Company, ever forward-looking and efficient, at once adopted this suggestion and incorporated it into their Egglestone and Stanhope mills. In 1802 a general instruction was sent to all their mills to provide a long ground-level flue between the furnace and the chimney base or stalk (the contemporary name for a chimney). Only a few years later, the Beaumont mills followed this lead, their first flue being built at the Allen mill in 1807. About 1845 the London Lead Company abandoned the horizontal chimney for a fume condenser in which the fumes had to pass up and down through faggots soaked in water. Yet between 1845 and 1850, under the guidance of Thomas Sopwith, the Allendale chimneys were being lengthened beyond any others in the country, to have a total run of over 8,000yd.

Although smelt mills have been thoroughly demolished at many sites, their flues can still be traced, though completely or partially collapsed. In total there are several miles of these flues in our area, one of the most interesting to follow being that of Langley Mill. This zigzags its way up the hill to a tall chimney which still dominates the countryside, though now looking rather dangerous at the top. Following the flue makes a pleasant walk and since the chimney is a good landmark it is the easiest point from which to begin tracing the flue. At first the flue appears, as it runs away from the chimney immediately across a field, to be nothing more than a marked line of parallel ridges and central depression. But after one crosses the road the stonework of the flue becomes more obvious, and as one follows it down the hill several complete stretches are found, about 3ft wide × 5ft high, which can easily be walked through (Plate, p 53). When the wood at the foot of the slope is reached, the collapsed flue unexpectedly turns and follows down the edge of the wood. At times it is almost lost in the heavy undergrowth and trees which hide its irregularities, but the strangest point comes when a railway cutting, now disued, is reached, for here the flue becomes a bridge to span the cutting. It once more sharply turns to follow the side of the cutting, tunnels under the approach slope of a farm-access bridge, doubles back unbelievably and is finally lost near the small dam of a reservoir.

What we have traced is in fact the original layout of the flue, which existed before the Hexham & Allendale Railway was constructed in 1864. At that time the flue was still in use and the railway proprietors were obliged to carry it in the form of a bridge across their cutting. Twenty-three years later the mill was dismantled, but the flue has remained. Fig 15 shows the lower stretches of the flue, and the mill buildings as they were in 1863 when the route for the railway was being surveyed.

This particular flue has been chosen as an interesting walk, but other flues have their own fascinating peculiarities: the 2½ miles of double flues from Allen Mill, long stretches being in good condition;

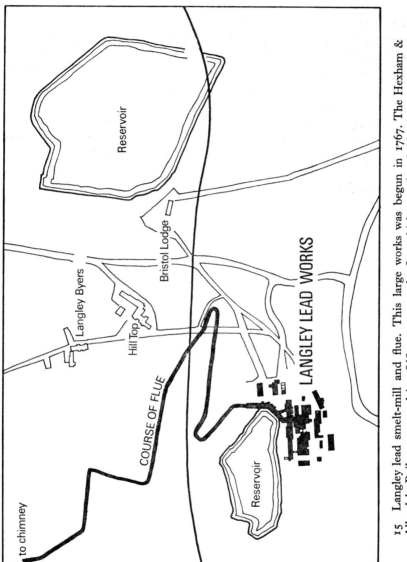

Reservoir

Langley Byers

Hill Top

Bristol Lodge

COURSE OF FLUE

to chimney

Reservoir

LANGLEY LEAD WORKS

15  Langley lead smelt-mill and flue. This large works was begun in 1767. The Hexham & Allendale Railway, opened in 1868, cut across the flue which was then bridged over a cutting. This drawing is based on a plan showing the proposed railway route (Northumberland Record Office)

the three short stretches of early flues at Stanhope which join and part in confusion at the top of the hill; the pair of fine 'gothic arches' which is all that remains at Dukesfield (Plate, p 53); the fine arch across the river and the long straight flue along the hillside at Rookhope; and the extraordinary maze which doubles up a small hill in a profusion of collapsed tunnels at Healeyfield Mill, Castleside (Fig 37). (This latter is now scheduled as an Ancient Monument.) So interesting are all these that one can recommend flue-walking (above-ground) as an interesting alternative to plain fell-walking!

*Notes to this chapter are on page* 197.

# CHAPTER FOUR

# *Iron and Steel*

### IRON MAKING

THE iron industry of the North East has undergone several violent fluctuations during the nineteenth and twentieth centuries and the current shrinkage is probably by no means complete.

A convenient proximity of iron ores and coal led to an early development of the industry and, when the local ores became exhausted or replaced by richer imported ores in the middle of the last century, some of the iron furnaces remained in operation for a number of years. But their number gradually dwindled as the economics of transport and larger production units took effect and today furnaces are to be found only at Consett, West Hartlepool and Middlesbrough (Teesside).

Iron is found as oxides, carbonates or suphides and the metal is obtained from the oxides by a chemical reaction shown as

$$Fe_2 O_3 + 3CO \longrightarrow 2 Fe + 3CO_2$$

The carbonates and sulphides are converted to oxides by a pre-heating or calcining. This is simply a heating of the ore, preparatory to it being charged in the blast furnace. Two changes are produced by calcination, chemical and physical. Any water present is expelled and carbonates are broken up completely, leaving ferric oxide and carbon dioxide; sulphides too are changed to oxides. All these reactions result in a more homogeneous material, more readily worked in the blast furnace. Very fine remains of stone-built calcining kilns together with their chimneys still stand in Rosedale to the south of the Cleveland Hills and Rosedale Chimney till recently was a noted landmark.

The reduction to metal from oxides is carried out in a blast furnace:

81

the gas, carbon monoxide, which performs this function is made by blowing hot air into burning coke. Other impurities associated with the ore combine with an added flux and are withdrawn as slag. From this will be seen that the requirements for a blast furnace are iron ore (as oxide), coke, flux (frequently limestone) and an air blast.

Blast furnaces have been built in many parts of the North East, but most have now disappeared. Over several centuries they have essentially had the same form and in the seventeenth and eighteenth centuries were roughly square, stone-built structures, charged at the top, and with air blown from bellows operated by waterwheel. A few late examples exist in this country, though none are known in the North East. A very good example is the furnace constructed in 1777 at Colebrookdale by Abraham Darby and preserved by Allied Iron-founders Ltd. As techniques improved furnaces were built taller and larger, and the greater air blast which they required was provided first by water-powered and later by steam-powered blowing engines. In 1828 James Neilson of Glasgow realised the value of heating the blast before admitting it to the furnace and this proved to be one of the greatest advances in the art of making iron. A very fine set of vertical steam-powered blowing engines stood until very recently, at the Middlesbrough Ayresome Works of Gjers Mills & Co, constructed between 1870 and 1872 (Fig 16).[1]

*Sources of iron ore*

In order to trace the early beginnings of the iron industry in the region, one needs to look at the sources of iron ore.[2] In southern Northumberland there have been several areas within the coal measures where blackband ironstone has been found in sufficient quantities to justify mining. These ores contain iron compounds, mingled with sufficient coaly matter to enable the ore to be calcined without the addition of coal. They are usually found in thin seams and their value as ores of iron was not realised until 1801 and it was some time before they were extensively used in the iron industry. The

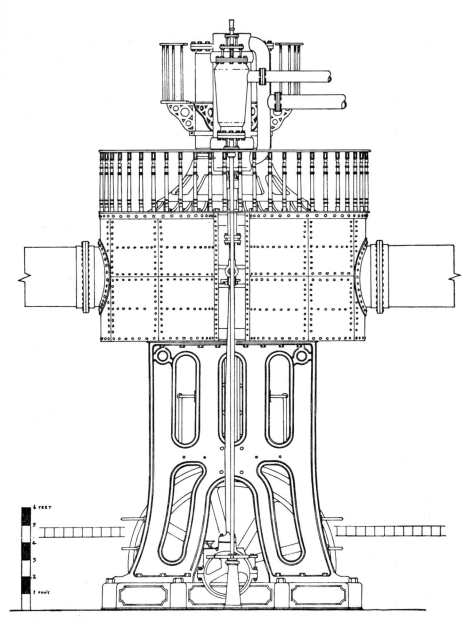

16   Ayresome Ironworks, Middlesbrough. One of three identical blast engines
built in 1870 to supply blast to the iron furnaces

two main areas of blackband ore have been on the North Tyne around Bellingham and on the South Tyne near Haydon Bridge.

In the Derwent Valley are occurrences of ironstone which have been locally utilised for several centuries, and it seems certain that somewhere between 1670 and 1710 a blast furnace and forge were erected at Allensford, only a mile or so to the west of the present large Consett works.

Along Weardale, spathose iron ore (iron carbonate) has been found, though somewhat irregularly, in the veins and flats of the lead mines. Until 1842 this ore had not been of much importance but in that year the Weardale Iron Company started to develop the industry. The important period of extraction continued until about 1880, though some activity continued for many years afterwards. It has been estimated that almost 2 million tons of iron ore have been produced from the area, most of it between 1842 and 1880. The proximity of this Weardale ore to the coalfield immediately to the east has played an important part in its exploitation.

In central Durham, ironstone has been found in close proximity to the coal, and collieries in the Pelton, Beamish, Washington and Lumley area were engaged from about 1830 to 1860 in raising this iron ore in addition to coal.

South-east of the river Tees the enormously rich ironstone of the Cleveland Hills, discovered in 1850, helped to develop Middlesbrough from a village to its present size, whilst still further south-east the ironstone nodules found in the Whitby-Scarborough area have been a source of iron over a much longer period. Being found on the coast, they were easily shipped to places where coal was abundant and thus helped to found the iron industry on the river Tyne.

### Distribution of blast furnaces

Having seen where iron ore has been found it is now possible to trace the logic of the distribution of early blast furnaces in Durham and Northumberland.[3] Probably one of the earliest sites within the region was that in the Derwent Valley at Allensford, already mentioned. Long before 1800 a furnace was erected at Whitehill, on Chester Burn about a mile to the west of Chester-le-Street. This furnace is of double interest, for not only does it seem probable that coke was used for smelting soon after its introduction for this purpose, but the ore smelted was partly imported from Robin Hood's Bay in the Whitby area, although local ore was in part used. Here we see for the first time the accessibility of a suitable seam of coal becoming a factor of predominating importance. The third of the early sites of iron smelting was at Bedlington, where the furnaces were probably built about 1737. The works attained great importance in the early part of the nineteenth century, were closed in 1855, reopened in 1861 and finally closed down in 1867.

Areas of iron smelting which developed during the nineteenth century were:

1  on the North and South Tyne, using local ores;
2  on the Tyne, mostly using imported ores;
3  in west and central Durham, mostly using local ores;
4  around Middlesbrough, using Cleveland ores.

Taking these in turn, and first looking at the *North and South Tyne*, blast furnaces were started by Messrs C. J. Bigge & Partners at Redesdale in 1839 and at Hareshaw nearer Bellingham in 1841 to smelt the ironstone found outcropping in both banks of Hareshaw Burn and extending over a considerable area of adjoining country. Coal was obtained from the tiny Plashetts coalfield towards the head of the North Tyne. The Redesdale furnaces were soon blown out, but the three at Hareshaw appear to have continued at work until about 1850. In about 1846 a blast furnace was erected at Chesterwood near Haydon Bridge, but this too did not continue in blast for long. All these furnaces only smelted local ores and they do not appear to have left any obvious remains.

*On the Tyne*, the next group of iron furnaces begins at Wylam where Christopher Blackett erected a blast furnace in 1836. This was leased in 1844 to the Bell Brothers who worked it until 1865 on Cleveland ironstone. This furnace is chiefly notable as the first venture of these brothers, famous not only as great ironmasters, but also on account of the great scientific attainments of the predominant partner, Sir Lowthian Bell, who founded the science of blast-furnace practice.

Further east along the Tyne iron smelting had been started at Lemington by the Tyne Iron Company in about 1795, to smelt local ores, but at an early date they were importing iron ore from Whitby. In 1871 this works was restarted as the Tyne Haematite Iron Company, using Spanish ore, but the Carlist War interfered with this supply and in 1876 the furnaces were finally blown out.

Still further down the Tyne, at Walker, were furnaces built in 1842 specifically to use the Whitby ore, in admixture with mill cinder. These, constructed by Losh, Wilson & Bell, were taken over by the Bell Bros in 1873 and continued in blast until about 1883. After a time they were again operated, but finally blown out in 1891.

On the south side of the Tyne, the well-known firm of Palmer's Shipbuilding Company was founded at Jarrow in 1851, at first as a shipbuilding yard, but in 1857 four blast furnaces were built. Mr Palmer (later Sir Charles Palmer) acquired a lease of ironstone royalties at Hinderwell between Saltburn and Whitby and this Cleveland ore was brought by ship to Jarrow. Port Mulgrave was constructed, near Hinderwell, for this trade.

Moving now to *west and central Durham*, it is not surprising to find that railway development in the mid 1800s produced a growing demand for iron products and played an important part in the setting up of works on the western edge of the coalfield at Consett, Tow Law and Witton Park. Until 1850 (when the rich part of the Cleveland iron ore was discovered) the location of inland blast furnaces was governed not only by the availability of suitable coking coal, but also of local or easily accessible supplies of iron ore from the western dales. The best coking coal in the region has come from west Durham and the presence of iron ores in Weardale, a little further to the west, naturally resulted in blast furnaces being put up in places accessible to both.

The Weardale ores, exploited by the Weardale Iron Company in 1842, were smelted first at Stanhope in 1845, and at Tow Law and Witton Park in 1846. The Stanhope furnace, although reputed to have produced high quality iron from the local ores, was only short-lived and was superseded by the Tow Law furnaces. Very slight traces remain by the side of the Stanhope Burn, below the Crawleyside lime kilns. Soon after the erection of these furnaces it became evident that the local ore supplies were inadequate and they were supplemented by Whitby ironstone.

In 1829 two furnaces were erected at Birtley, to smelt ironstone from the surrounding collieries of Pelton, Beamish, Washington, Harraton and Lumley, and continued in blast until 1867. Other blast furnaces in Durham were put up at Tudhoe in 1853 and Ferry-hill in 1858.

The Consett ironworks was originally established in 1840 under the name of the Derwent Iron Company, to smelt local ironstones which occur in so many places in the Derwent Valley and which had probably been worked during the seventeenth and eighteenth centuries. It is worthy of note that the Consett Iron Company's works are the only ones remaining of all those mentioned above and all their ore is now imported.

Finally, the *Middlesbrough-Cleveland area* needs to be looked at, for here are a few remains of interest to the industrial archaeologist. Iron has been made within the area from medieval times and the monks at Guisborough and Rievaulx had their bloomeries and forges, some of which continued in use into the seventeenth century. In 1745 ironstone nodules, which were abundant on the foreshore around Robin Hood's Bay, are known to have been sent by coastal boats to the river Wear and taken upstream to Whitehill furnace near Chester-le-Street. In about 1795 ironstone nodules were being taken from the shore at Scarborough and Saltburn and soon the ironstone was being mined from beds which outcropped on the coastal cliffs. Tracing these outcrops inland, the great ore-field around Guisborough and along the northern flanks of the Cleveland Hills was found. John Vaughan, who had entered partnership with Henry Bolckow and built an ironworks at Witton Park in 1846, discovered ironstone on the Eston Hills in 1850. Quarrying began only nine weeks later and the first blast furnace was built in Middlesbrough in 1851.

In Durham the discovery of Cleveland iron ore led to further furnaces being erected: at Washington in 1856, by Messrs Bell Brothers (until 1875); at Ferryhill in 1858, by James Morison (until 1882); at Middleton St George in 1867; at West Hartlepool in 1874; at Stockton in 1873; at Darlington about 1850 (until 1876); at Norton by Messrs John Rogerson & Company (until 1877). The Port Clarence ironworks were started by Bell Brothers in 1853 and taken over subsequently by Messrs Dorman & Long. The magnificent office block and adjoining blast-engine house still remain though badly ruined (Plate, p 71).

The Cleveland area may be examined for industrial remains in three main areas: to the north around Eston and Guisborough where the greatest mining has been done (see Aysdalegate, Boosbeck, Lingdale and Skelton in Gazetteer); to the east round Hinderwell where earlier mining began, and continued through the nineteenth century; and to the south in Rosedale where ore was mined and calcined until recent years.[4] Mention of remaining structures and buildings in these areas will be found in the Gazetteer.

STEEL MAKING

The primary products of the iron and steel industry are three: pig iron or cast iron, malleable or wrought iron, and steel; and although chemically quite similar they have in fact very dissimilar properties.[5] *Pig iron* is the product of the blast furnace and is so called from the form of the moulds into which the molten metal was poured, these smaller moulds lying at right angles to the main trough or 'sow' through which the metal ran. Thus the appearance was given of a

Page 89 (right)
*Pottery kiln near
Corbridge. This is
probably the only
pottery 'bottle kiln' left
in the region*

(left) *an eighteenth-
century steel
cementation furnace
near Rowlands
Gill. Believed to be
the only remaining
eighteenth-century
furnace of its
kind, this is scheduled
for preservation
by the Regional Open
Air Museum*

Page 90  (left) *Tower mill at Elwick. A finely built brick structure with much of the machinery remaining, though quite inaccessible, on the upper floors;* (below) *Craster: a shrunken port. The squat stone structure is the foundation of a tower carrying overhead stone-loading gear. All stone shipments have ceased, but Craster is still famous for its kippers*

litter of piglets lying suckling at the sow. Molten iron from the blast furnace is nowadays taken in bulk for steel making and very rarely run into pigs. Pig iron or cast iron may contain up to 5 per cent of impurity, mostly carbon. It can be used for casting, as one of its names implies, since it expands on solidification, but it is brittle, cannot be welded, and will not sustain heavy loads.

*Malleable or wrought iron* is simply cast iron from which the impurities, particularly the carbon, have been almost entirely removed. Wrought iron is tough and, before the invention of the Bessemer process in 1855 for making steel, was of much greater importance than it is today. Little is now produced, but it is a delight to any craftsman for hot working, and is greatly prized. When strongly heated it becomes plastic and so can be hammered into any required form, and separate portions can be united by welding. Wrought iron is made by heating pig iron in a reverberatory furnace where the carbon and other impurities are slowly oxidised away. As the carbon is removed the melting point of the purer iron rises and the metal, at first liquid, begins to 'ball together' or solidify to a pasty mass. This is taken from the furnace whilst hot and hammered to consolidate it and to drive out the slag and impurities, and the result, ready for reheating and rolling to the required bar shape, is wrought iron. It shows, if cut, a distinct lamination.

*Steel* is iron containing less than about 1·5 per cent of carbon. Before Bessemer's invention it was made from wrought iron and carbon by the laborious cementation process (or by Huntsman's crucible process), but after 1855 the Bessemer converter came into general use. The converter is a vessel in which air is blown through molten cast iron, so eliminating the intermediate processes of wrought-iron preparation. The Bessemer converter itself has now been superseded, and only one example remains in the North East, in the works of Consett Iron Company, and this is likely to be demolished shortly.

Cementation is a process which has a long history, being the fusing of very small quantities of pure carbon with hot wrought iron. When

F

charcoal was used for firing, a bar of iron would not only be heated by the fire, but could absorb a minute amount of pure carbon. However, when, by the seventeenth century, charcoal was becoming too scarce to waste in this way, coal fires had to be used. Yet coal contains many impurities, and sulphur in particular was found to combine with the iron and so form a brittle undesirable product. Towards the end of the seventeenth century it was found that if wrought-iron bars were placed in large stone or earthenware boxes, packed in charcoal and sealed on top, they could be successfully heated in a coal fire. Thus the converting or cementation furnace was devised.

Records suggest that this process began to be developed early in the eighteenth century and, around 1700, steel making was introduced into the North East probably from Stourbridge, by Sir Ambrose Crowley. Some sixty years later when the French investigator, Gabriel Jars, visited the North East he observed cementation furnaces at work and described and illustrated one in his book *Voyages Métallurgiques*. Furnaces of this type were in ever-diminishing use in Sheffield until about 1939, but the last one in our region seems to have been finally discontinued towards the end of the last century. It still stands at Hamsterley Colliery (qv) near Rowlands Gill, is locally known as Derwentcote, and probably dates from the early or middle years of the eighteenth century. It is built of stone and practically identical in every respect with the record left by Gabriel Jars (Plate, p 89).

It is not inappropriate to mention at this point John Gjers of Middlesbrough, a nineteenth-century innovator of some note in the iron and steel industry. The Ayresome works of Gjers Mills & Co has already been mentioned (p 82) and it is unfortunate that it, containing so many examples of Gjers' work, has only recently been entirely destroyed. Gjers introduced, for example, the concept of a soaking pit in 1882 in which a newly cast ingot of steel could be stored, without great heat loss, whilst achieving a constant distribution of heat throughout its mass. He also constructed several sets of a remarkable exhausting engine which, by steam power, exhausted the air from 'pots' and operated vacuum hoists for raising to a height furnace charges and materials for hopper-storage.

IRON WORKING

*Village smithies*

One of the longest lived crafts in the world is that of the blacksmith and it is only in the last fifty years or less that it has been finally eclipsed. Working with hot wrought iron, the smith was able to make the most intricate or massive objects by the clever combination of a limited number of techniques: bending, thickening, welding, and fulling or shaping.[6] He made his own tools and all the miscellaneous ironwork required around the village: gate-fittings, farm implements, domestic items, cart-wheel tyres, chains and nails. Gradually some parts of his work, such as chain-making and nail-making, became more specialised, and evolved into separate crafts. Yet it has always remained true that the blacksmith was a jack-of-all-trades, able to carry out a much wider range of skills than his more specialised colleagues and differing from them only in speed of production.

The village smithy was an essential feature of a village and the small single-storey building, often centrally placed, can frequently still be identified even though converted to a garage or outhouse. The contents of a smithy are probably too well known to merit lengthy mention and many museums have set up a small reconstruction, with hand-operated, pear-shaped bellows slung in their gallows by the hearth and the nearby anvil. The tools of the smith, although made by himself for his own use, are yet surprisingly constant in their general shape throughout the country. He requires hammers, tongs, swages and fullers (to shape the hot iron) over a wide range of sizes and shapes.

In some parts of the countryside the smith's work was wide and varied, in others he might spend a very large proportion of his time on farriery. Larger farms in rich agricultural areas employed so many horses and implements as to necessitate a smith permanently on the farm; in other areas a small smithy in the farm buildings would be visited weekly by a journeying smith.

In Northumberland and North Yorkshire several smithies have dated headstones or doorways and sometimes the horseshoe motif is carved in the stone. These attractive features mostly date from the first half of the nineteenth century and good examples are at Seave Green, Yorkshire, where '1826' is split by a small horseshoe over the door; at Scremerston (Northumberland) where a similar small shoe has been linked with the possible date of 1840 (now indecipherable) on the gable; at Ponteland, near Newcastle, where the date 1822 is boldly stated over the door (Plate, p 72); and at Ford, also in Northumberland, where an enormous stone horseshoe makes the door surround of 1863. This latter is not a typical smithy, but part of the model village built by Louisa Marchioness of Waterford to the east of the grounds of the castle where she lived as a young widow.

Two other features often to be recognised even when smithies are no longer in use are both associated with cart-wheels. A large heavy circular iron plate of perhaps 5ft diameter with a central hole of about 15in is often to be seen lying at ground level outside the smithy door. This is a tyring plate and on it rested the wooden cart-wheel, gripped in position while its iron hoop or tyre was shrunk on. The other more obvious object is a tyre-bender, built to help the smith shape a lengthy iron strip into a circle which would then have its ends welded to make the wheel tyre. Good examples, all in Northumberland, can be seen at Scremerston, Shilbottle, and New York (near North Shields) where small iron pieces are attached to stout upright posts set firmly in the ground, and at Riding Mill where the ironwork is bolted to a well-shaped stone upright. At Romaldkirk smithy on the Yorkshire bank of the Tees, the ironwork was leaded into a squarish stone block set nearer ground level.[7] Perhaps the Northumberland smiths did not like stooping!

*Nails, chains and files*

Several specialised crafts have developed from that of the smith and been active in the North East, but all have now ceased operation and their traces are few.

Nails have been needed for almost as long as wood has been used, as a Scottish 'find' a few years ago of 5 tons of Roman nails demonstrates. These Roman nails varied from 6 or 7in long to less than 1in and are practically indistinguishable from their nineteenth-century handmade counterparts. Probably a number of foundries at one time also made nails, certainly they have been made in large quantities at Wolsingham in Weardale and at Winlaton (qv). At the latter village a small nail-shop has been preserved *in situ* by the local council and it is hoped eventually to have this fully equipped and open to the public.

Winlaton was also, until recent years, the home of other specialised iron-working crafts such as clog-iron making, lock-making and chain-smithing. These crafts formed an interesting remnant of early eighteenth-century industrial development. In 1691 Ambrose Crowley took a lease on land at Winlaton, where he set up works to make nails: his story has been well told by Michael Flinn in *Men of Iron*, 1962.[8] The business prospered and Crowley obtained substantial naval contracts mainly for sheathing nails which were his speciality. (The sheathing of ships' hulls with copper sheets remained for long too costly for practical purposes, and thin wooden sheaths, requiring vast quantities of sheathing nails, were mainly used for the purpose.) Crowley expanded into other items of ironware and the family business prospered to the end of the eighteenth century, making all kinds of ironware, nails, locks, clog-irons and chains. In 1782 the business became known as Crowley, Millington & Company but in 1815 the end of the Napoleonic Wars reduced the Admiralty contracts for anchors, chains etc, leading to the closing of the Winlaton works in 1816. This closure caused something of a social upheaval and skilled workmen were reputed to have migrated to Sheffield and Rotherham, where it was later claimed that 'many of the most distinguished iron works in these towns owe their rise in no small measure to the superior ingenuity and information imported by emigrants from Crowley and Company's workshops'.[9] Of those that remained in Winlaton some contrived to maintain a livelihood as independent domestic craftsmen and, surprisingly, several of the resultant small businesses carried on until the middle of this century.

The very last chain-maker (Plate, p 72) retired in 1966 having worked at his craft in Winlaton for over fifty years and so ended the iron trade which began there in 1691. The contents of this last shop have been taken into store for use in the Regional Open Air Museum and the last example of earlier workshops, 'Bagnolds' shop', has likewise now been dismantled and stored.

When Ambrose Crowley set up his works at Winlaton, it was because he had decided to move away from Sunderland where he had earlier tried to start in about 1682. Apparently labour difficulties caused him to leave Sunderland, but that town continued to grow and at least one iron-working industry there has had a long history of hand-working, namely file-cutting. The present firm of Cook & Nicholson has developed from the hand-worked trade although nothing is believed to remain except a few hand tools. The file-cutter's hammer is unique in shape on account of the unusual 'pecking' action necessary to raise up the file-teeth, and it is therefore interesting to remark that a small ironworks at Wolsingham in Weardale still contains a quantity of such hammers, which were once a speciality of the area.

Another iron-working craft now completely ended was that of spade-forging at Ford Forge in Northumberland. The old water-powered forge has now been gutted and all that remains is the shell of the building and a few wooden templates rescued for the Regional Open Air Museum.

*Notes to this chapter are on page 198.*

# CHAPTER FIVE

# *Other Minerals*

MINERALS of less economic importance to the region than coal, lead and iron have nevertheless played some part in its history, and others are perhaps destined to play a larger part in its future.

## *Copper and witherite*

To deal first with those minerals which are now almost or completely worked out, mention must be made of copper deposits at Middleton Tyas in Yorkshire. Here was an occurrence of copper in sufficient quantity to support a small but thriving industry in the mid-eighteenth century, but as all work on the deposit ceased by about 1780 it has passed almost into oblivion.

There are two documentary sources to its short-lived history: a series of letters in the collection of the North East Institute of Mining Engineers written by the Newcastle engine-builder William Brown who, between 1752 and 1754, was consulted about the erection of pumping-gear at the Middleton Tyas mines,[1] and an account of a visit to the mines in 1765 written by the French industrial 'spy' Gabriel Jars in his book *Voyages Métallurgiques*.[2] From these it seems that the mines were opened up in about 1750, the first being on a very small scale in the glebe lands, and initiated by the Rev John Mawer. (A memorial tablet to his death in 1763 is in the nearby church.) Shortly afterwards two rival companies were mining the area, one with miners imported from Derbyshire, the other mainly with Cornishmen.

By 1754 at least one 'Fire-Engine' (the contemporary name for a Newcomen-type steam pumping-engine) was installed and there were two smelting furnaces burning about 18 tons of coal each week. The ore was assayed and produced 14cwt of malleable copper from 21cwt of ore. When Jars visited the site in 1765 production was already past its best and he noted that the mines were very small and irregular and 'ought rather to be called fox-earths than mines'. By 1800 it was possible for a writer to describe the industry as having flourished some time ago, being represented by traces of mounds and fire-burned stones from the furnaces. Until about 1950 the engine-house erected in 1753 stood at the south-east end of the churchyard, with a group of houses in the village called Smelt Mill houses. Now it is just possible to trace the earth mounds of the shafts in a field adjoining the churchyard.

To move further to the north of our region, Fallowfield mines in Northumberland, $2\frac{1}{2}$ miles north of Hexham, have a recorded history of over 300 years.

The first documentary reference to these mines is in 1611, but it seems likely that they were worked earlier than this, perhaps even in Roman times. They were first worked for lead, which at one time was smelted on the site, and there are accounts in existence for 1681 recording the purchase of a waterwheel, bellows and hearthstones. In the mid-eighteenth century, however, when the miners enjoyed considerable prosperity, the ore was carried by pack pony to the smelt mill at Acton, some nine miles to the south and parts of this track can still be traced. In the early years of the nineteenth century the mines were none too prosperous but a remarkable revival in their fortune took place in the 1840s when working for witherite and barytes began. Witherite is a natural carbonate of barium which occurs in this form in only a few places in the world. Barium sulphate, generally known as barytes, is the more common, related mineral. Fallowfield was probably the first commercial mine for witherite in this country, if not in the world, and along with one other at Settling-stones, five miles further west, remained one of the two main sources in the British Isles. It closed in 1913, and Settlingstones closed in 1969. A more detailed description of the mines (on which the above paragraphs are based) and the site as it is today has been written by Fred Brook for the *Journal of Industrial Archaeology*. Fig 17 is taken from that paper.[3]

## Salt

If the scant copper and scarce witherite of the region are completely or almost worked out, there are other minerals currently being extracted or ripe for exploitation. Amongst the mineral resources of North-East England salt yields first place only to coal. In the seventeenth and eighteenth centuries, salt was extracted from sea water (p 114). The large-scale salt industry of the present day, however, started with the discovery of rock salt on Teesside. This was an accidental discovery, made when a bore was put down at Middlesbrough in 1859 by Messrs Bolckow, Vaughan & Co Ltd to seek water. At a depth of 1,200ft a 100ft thick bed of rocksalt was struck. No immediate use was made of this chance find until after 1874, when salt was again struck by Messrs Bell Bros at Port Clarence on the other side of the river. From then on the annual output rose steadily until in 1894 the total production of the Middlesbrough district exceeded 300,000 tons.

The saltfield district is bleak, low-lying and featureless and little remains of this early industry except to the north at Greatham where a wooden-beamed brine pump survives; promised for the Regional Open Air Museum. Pumping ceased here in 1969.

## Gypsum

Gypsum (a form of calcium sulphate) is another mineral found around Teesside and is now used chiefly for the manufacture of plaster of paris and plaster-board for the building trade. Old records of the Thirsk area indicate that it was found, as much as 40ft thick, when wells were being sunk, though here it was rather more marly (ie mixed with clay) than pure gypsum. Names such as Plasterpit

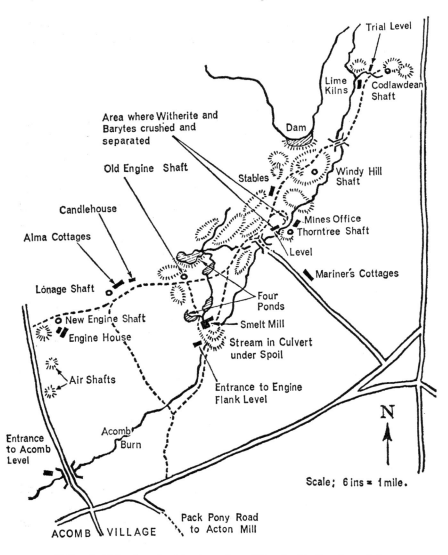

Trial Level

Lime
Kilns

Codlawdean
Shaft

Area where Witherite and
Barytes crushed and
separated

Dam

Old Engine Shaft

Stables

Windy Hill
Shaft

Candlehouse

Mines Office
Thorntree Shaft

Alma Cottages

Level

Mariner's Cottages

Lónage Shaft

Four
Ponds

New Engine Shaft

Smelt Mill

Engine House

Stream in Culvert
under Spoil

Air Shafts

Entrance to Engine
Flank Level

N

Entrance
to Acomb
Level

Acomb
Burn

Scale: 6 ins = 1 mile.

Pack Pony Road
to Acton Mill

ACOMB VILLAGE

17   Fallowfield lead and witherite mine. (Plan by F. Brook, 1967)

House indicate however that a certain amount may have been extracted for plastering purposes.

## Potash

Potash salts have currently been proved to exist in considerable quantity inland from Whitby, having first been discovered when a trial for oil was made near there in 1939. Further extensive working can therefore be expected in an area which has remained relatively aloof from industrial exploitation.

### OBTAINED BY QUARRYING

Quarrying has left its mark in the region, though the industrial archaeologist will generally find little in the way of buildings or machinery on the sites. There are a variety of rocks which have been sought at one time or another.

Limestone was quarried on a small scale wherever lime was to be burnt for agricultural purposes and these tiny quarries are always associated with their small kilns. Quarrying on a larger scale, for the commercial production of lime and also Portland cement, is mentioned when lime kilns are described at greater length (p 102).

Grindstones have been, and for that matter still are, worked from a fine-grained stone quarried along the Tyne. In the seventeenth century a popular phrase ran: 'A Scot, a Rat and a New-Castle Grindstone, you may find all the World over.'[4] The stone so suitable for this purpose is a massive sandstone, Newcastle Grindstone, outcropping to the south-east of Newcastle. Here, at Springwell near Gateshead, strata totalling 120ft in thickness are still quarried. The top 60ft of stone overburden is taken off and used for road foundations, leaving 60ft of high-grade sandstone with close-bonded silica particles which is particularly suited to the production of grindstones and building stone.[5]

As early as 1519 the records of the Newcastle Merchant Adventurers show that grindstones from Tyneside quarries were being exported widely, and the forerunners of the present quarry owners at Gateshead had a big trade in the 1880s with Russia, Europe, the Americas and the Colonies. These stones were used for general engineering, sharpening the field tools of the sugar plantations, shelling rice and wood pulping for the paper industry.

Other rocks quarried for building purposes were various freestones and slates, while whinstone was quarried for road-making wherever it conveniently outcropped.

A small but curious and interesting local industry was the production of slate pencils or, more correctly, shale pencils for use on writing slates. At the foot of Cronkley Scar on the Yorkshire bank of the river Tees is a small area of pre-Devonian shale brought up by heavy faulting of the rocks. This shale was apparently ideal for making pencils and nearby stand the ruins of the Cronkley (or Widdy Bank) 'Pencil Mill', measuring about 50ft × 20ft. It would seem that the shale was ground, and presumably subsequently compressed or moulded into pencil shape, for there are traces of a wheel-pit and leat and close to them lie a pair of small millstones. An 1899 guide[6] to walks up the Tees mentions the mill as being then already deserted, though there are references in the Strathmore estate papers in the 1870s and 1880s to the Widdy Bank slate quarry and its possible lease at £5 or £10 per annum.[7]

It may be of interest to comment here that in Durham dialect the word pencil meant a pencil for use on a slate, whereas a lead pencil (such as one uses today) was known as a 'vine' or a 'keelyvine'. Elderly people still recollect a copying-ink pencil being called an 'ink-vine'.

### Lime kilns

Limestone is, in practical terms, insoluble and therefore of no use for liming or de-acidifying agricultural land. When crushed limestone is strongly heated, however, it becomes chemically changed to quicklime, and the application of water to this yields slaked lime which is fairly soluble. During the sixteenth century the value of lime as a dressing for sour land was discovered and seventeenth-century books on agriculture frequently mention its use. By the early-eighteenth century we find several writers telling farmers how to construct and operate their kilns.[8] A simple method, long used by small farmers, was akin to charcoal-burning; the farmer would build a fire and heap on broken limestone and fuel, covering the whole with turf and leaving it to smoulder for a day or two. The resultant ashes would be rich in lime and potash and sufficient for a season's liming. For the small farmer there was therefore little need for a permanent stone-built kiln, and such small kilns as now remain from the eighteenth and early-nineteenth centuries on our limestone hillsides were probably operated on a commercial basis. Many were indeed probably worked in the summer months by leadminers as a healthful change from their underground labours.

These small kilns can be found scattered across the upland lime-stone hillsides wherever a small outcrop of rock conveniently occurs. They were generally built into a hillside, just below the outcrop, taking advantage of the natural slope so that barrow-loads of fuel and broken stone could be tipped in above and the calcined products drawn out below. The interior of the kiln, generally circular or some-times oval in plan, narrowed downwards. A description of a north-country kiln written by William Marshall in 1788 states:[9]

> The materials are either limestone entirely or limestone lined with bricks, and no other air-holes are made than the 'eyes' at which they are kindled. The form of the cavity is an irregular cone inverted. At the bottom are generally two eyes opposite to each other, the cavity being here contracted to a narrow trough, the width of the eyes. The proportion between the depths and the diameters of these kilns is that of the depth being generally about one and a half diameter of the top. The size varies from six to 40 chaldrons [a chaldron was about 50cwt].

Even the large industrial kilns still to be found operating by this system in parts of County Durham are fundamentally constructed in the same way, though of course much larger and fired by coke.

Marshall discussed fuel for the kiln already described and wrote:

> The morelands for the last fifty years have furnished coals for lime-burning. The seam of this coal is thin and the quality very ordinary. Before the discovery of these coals, lime was burnt with furze and other brushwood. About three chaldrons of lime are burnt from one chaldron of coals.

Such thin seams of poor quality coal are not uncommon in the limestone areas and would clearly play a part in the siting of the kilns.

Although lime from these kilns was sold and carried some distance by pack horse in the eighteenth and early-nineteenth centuries, it was a bulky commodity and not likely to be transported more than a few miles. Where, however, limestone occurred on the coast and especially when fuel was fairly near at hand, lime could be exported, for at that period the only practical means of long-distance bulk transport was by water. Only two points on the Northumberland coast fulfilled these conditions: Seahouses and Beadnell. Elsewhere on the limestone coast no natural harbours existed and the only other likely point, Craster, is built on the Whin Sill, a hard rock suitable only for roadstone. At both Seahouses and Beadnell still stand fine eighteenth-century groups of kilns which must once have served a flourishing export trade. At the former is constructed a long bank of seven kilns facing to sea, whilst at Beadnell four very large kilns were constructed in circular fashion, each with three or four archways for extracting the lime. To allow an earthen charging-ramp to lead to the top of the kilns and yet give full access to the burnt lime, at the four points, tunnels were constructed (Fig 18). This fine set of kilns is now in the care of the National Trust and has been reasonably restored and well preserved from further depredation by the sea. The circular plan of the Beadnell kilns seems to be rather unusual in the North East, and another example near Rennington, about nine miles away, suggests a local style.

The coming of the railway system in the mid-nineteenth century made it possible to transport large quantities of lime from inland areas and we find many large kilns being constructed adjoining the

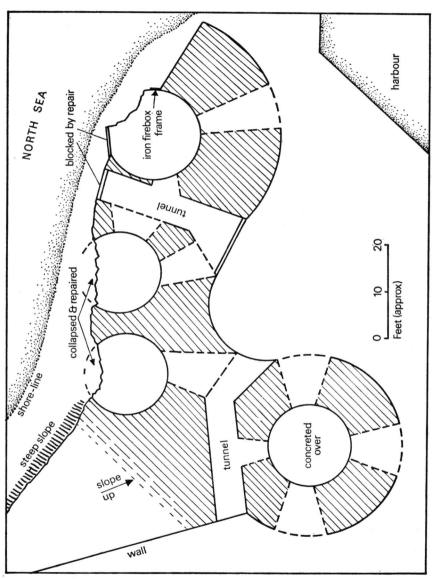

NORTH SEA

shore-line

steep slope

slope up

collapsed & repaired

blocked by repair

iron firebox frame

tunnel

tunnel

wall

tunnel

concreted over

harbour

0    10    20

Feet (approx)

18  Plan of lime kilns at Beadnell. From these eighteenth-century kilns, lime was exported down the coast

main lines. One very good example is that near Rennington, in Northumberland. It comprises eight huge kilns oval in shape and designed expressly for loading into rail trucks, for a spur rail ran down the centre of the structure with kilns discharging towards it on each side; the whole being under cover. This building is almost 30ft at its highest point and the rail entry was through a fine arched opening. The spur rail has now been lifted and deterioration has set in. Other rail-linked lime kilns are at East Layton (Yorkshire), Humshaugh (Northumberland) and Stanhope and Ferryhill (County Durham), the latter kiln being still operational, built of stone and repaired in brick.

At least one railway system was built across County Durham in part to transport lime: the Stanhope & Tyne line which began at kilns in limestone quarries just to the north of Stanhope and by means of stationary haulage engines, self-acting inclines, horse- and locomotive-worked line, transported lime and coal to South Shields. En route, lime was stored for sale to local farmers and one good example of a lime and coal depot (1834) stood recently at West Boldon level crossing. The kilns at Stanhope where this lime was burnt are well worth examination (Fig 19). Here are two periods of kilns: small circular ones of about 1834 built by the Stanhope & Tyne Railway Company, and much larger oval ones built more than ten years later by the Stockton & Darlington Railway Company. The former were apparently charged by hand, whereas to the top of the latter ran a rail-line for the larger-scale operating which their size demanded.

Lime was not used only for agricultural purposes. A great part of all lime burnt was used, with sand and water, as the building material called mortar, and the first step taken in the construction of many large buildings was the making of a kiln as near at hand as possible. A late example of this practice occurred when the large building of the Bowes Museum at Barnard Castle was begun in 1869, for a kiln was built on the nearest limestone, near the river Tees about a mile away.

Portland cement, invented in 1824, is made by strongly heating a

Page 107  (above) *Abutment of the Gaunless Bridge, Stockton & Darlington Railway,
1825. The first iron railway bridge, crossing the river Gaunless, sprang from here. The
bridge is preserved in the National Transport Collection, York; (below) railway goods
shed at Belford. A typical example in the region, though now rather rare*

Page 108 (left
The Union Bria
on the river
Tweed. Linking
Scotland and
Northumberland
this bridge was
constructed in 18
and is the earlie
surviving suspen
sion bridge in th
country

(right) the
Lintzford Bridge.
This elegant
eighteenth-century
bridge now gives
access to a paint
works, once a
paper mill

mixture of limestone and clay and a modern cement works has now
invaded Weardale, whilst another operates near Coxhoe.

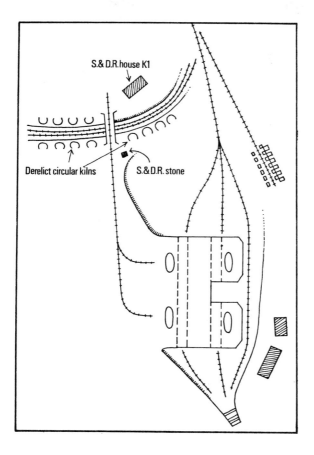

19  Sketch-plan of lime kilns at Crawleyside, near Stanhope.
These kilns stood at the western end of the Stanhope & Tyne
Railway. The smaller circular kilns were replaced by the much
larger oval kilns

G

## BRICKS AND POTTERY

In several parts of the North East are materials which have been mined or quarried for crushing, moulding and firing to produce bricks and earthenware commodities. Various shales, clays and fireclays are associated with the Coal Measures and some are still in use while others have been worked out or are no longer of competitive quality.

Brickmaking and tile-making, once a large regional industry, has contracted and many derelict brickworks dot the countryside usually near to a flooded clay pit. Probably the earliest visible remains are those of a stone-built kiln, dating possibly from the late-eighteenth century, near Mickleton in Teesdale. Here the square chimney still stands and the foundations of the oval kiln, about 55ft long, show traces of a surrounding underground flue. Until about five years ago one end of the kiln remained standing, showing its elegant construction (Fig 20). Early brick or tile kilns still remain at Belsay and Capheaton, Northumberland. Typical examples of more recent closures are at Ponteland, Northumberland, where two Newcastle kilns still stand with their chimneys, and at Stockton-on-Tees, where the Portrack Brickworks stands forlorn, below a recent housing estate. Here are both round kilns and Newcastle ones, with a variety of chimneys.

The Newcastle kiln may be the North East's chief contribution to the industrial history of brickmaking. It was an intermittent kiln and has therefore been replaced in more recent years by the Staffordshire continuous kiln. The plan was rectangular with the fire at one end and a rather squat chimney at the other (Fig 21). Unlike subsequent kiln developments, where the waste gases are utilised in pre-drying and pre-heating 'green' bricks, the heat from each burning cycle of the Newcastle kiln was completely lost. It is interesting to note, however, that even today a few Newcastle kilns are occasionally to be found still in use at quite large brickworks. This is on account of two

20   Brick kiln at Mickleton. This sketch is based on a
photograph taken in 1960. The stone-built kiln has now
entirely collapsed, though its plan can still be observed

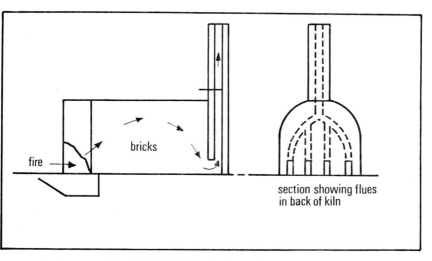

fire

bricks

section showing flues
in back of kiln

21   'Newcastle' brick kiln. Idealised sections of a late nineteenth-
century kiln

slight advantages which they have over large continuous kilns: various attractive effects can be obtained more readily and, since the burning cycle is only twelve days, earlier delivery can be made of special bricks which are urgently required.[10]

Up to only a few years ago coarse pottery was made in all three north-eastern counties and some of these wares achieved at least local fame. The Linthorpe Pottery near Middlesbrough produced an over-decorated and, at any rate to modern eyes, deplorably designed, coarse, glazed-ware of which a large collection may be seen in the Dorman Museum, Teesside. Canny Hill Pottery near Bishop Auckland was a less well-known local pottery, and a larger one was the Tyne or South Shields Pottery established in Waterloo Vale in 1830.

There are few visible remains of such potteries. Near Corbridge are the only good examples in the North East of large pottery kilns of the type once familiar in the Midland potteries landscape. Two large, brick, bottle-shaped kilns now stand semi-derelict, not having been used for many years. A nearby householder has dug up in his garden several good examples of their ware, which was apparently mostly small earthenware bottles of the type once used to hold ink, and larger items of sanitary ware. Near the two large kilns stand a circular kiln and two Newcastle brick kilns.

Although there is now no pottery manufacturer left in the region, Messrs Adamsez of Lemington, to the west of Newcastle, produce fine sanitary ware and there are small works at Prudhoe, Bardon Mill, and at Blaydon in County Durham, making coarse sanitary ware, earthenware pipes and fittings. At several of these works older parts can still be traced and at Bardon Mill, for example, one circular dome-topped kiln continues in use together with three modified Newcastle kilns.

White earthenware, a much finer product attempting to simulate porcelain and first produced commercially by Josiah Wedgwood, was introduced to County Durham between 1730 and 1740, at Carr's Hill Pottery near Gateshead. Development was rapid and soon four potteries were at work on Gateshead Fell. White clay, necessary to this process, was cheap and abundant for it was brought from Devon and Cornwall as ballast by vessels transporting coal from the Tyne. Other works sprang up on the Wear and a large export trade to north-east Europe developed in the early-nineteenth century. There were two potteries at Southwick: that of Antony Scott established in 1788 and dismantled in 1896, and the Wear Pottery founded in 1789 and discontinued in the late-nineteenth century; one at North Hylton (1762 to 1817); the Low Ford Pottery at South Hylton; and Sunderland or Garrison Pottery established in 1807. This latter firm was especially noted for its pink lustre ware.[11]

The North Hylton firm was removed in 1817 to Newcastle and there, as C. T. Maling & Sons Ltd of Ford Pottery, it continued working until only a few years ago.[12] Its buildings, one certainly of 1878, are now occupied as warehouses. This was the first pottery in the North East to produce printed transfer ware. After transference to the Ford Pottery, the firm continued to prosper to such an extent that the existing premises were unable to cope with demands and in 1859 larger premises were built on the same site. Trade continued to be good and in 1878 an even larger pottery was built on an adjoining site and it is this large, solidly built structure which is now occupied by Messrs Hoults as a furniture store.

This white-earthenware industry of the eighteenth and nineteenth centuries required as one of its basic materials, ground calcined flint to serve as aggregate to the white clay, and this demand led to the construction of water-powered flint-grinding mills. At such a mill, blocks of stone were pushed around a stone-paved circular pan of perhaps 10 to 15ft diameter. Horizontal arms were fixed to an upright central shaft and so moved the stone blocks within the slurry pan to crush the calcined flint. Flint-grinding mills of this description may still be found in Cornwall and Staffordshire and several worked at one time in the North East, though no buildings are now recognisable here, and can only be traced from records and from nineteenth-century OS maps. For example the fast-flowing Ouseburn, tributary to the Tyne, drove several flint mills including those at Jesmond

Dene, at Deep Dane House, at Millfield House and at lower Ouseburn (between Byker Bridge and the Ouseburn railway viaduct). This latter mill was part of the Stepney Pottery. On the opposite bank of the stream are the derelict remains of a steam-driven flint mill and pot bank (p 256 of Gazetteer). In County Durham there were at least three: one near Whitehill, one near Fencehouses and a third near Beamish. All these were kept employed supplying the Wearside potteries, and Pockerley flint mill near Beamish, in particular, was leased to Moore & Co of the Wear Pottery at Southwick. Though no trace of the Pockerley buildings can be seen, the rockery of a nearby cottage contains several flat-faced stones which probably came out of the slurry pan.

### SALT FROM THE SEA

It is almost certainly too late to find remnants of an industry which once blackened the sky of the north-east coast and consumed a quarter of a million tons of coal annually: namely the making of salt from sea water. South Shields, in the mid-eighteenth century, was the centre of this thriving industry and it is very faintly possible that traces of one of the salt-pans will be observed during the course of current development there. So far none has been recorded, but has anyone looked and watched closely?

At the time of the Domesday Book, salt was being made on the south coast by burning wood to evaporate sea water.[13] As coal began to be mined in the north we find references to its use for salt making on the north-east coast. Early mention of salt making there cannot be proved to refer to the use of coal, but in 1463 the monks of Tynemouth obtained a charter from Edward IV for loading and unloading their own and other ships, to enable them to trade freely in coals and white salt. An early reference to iron salt-pans at South Shields occurs in 1499, though lead continued in use as the chief construction material for some time after.

In 1635 Sir William Brereton[14] travelled through the North of England and in June he went to 'Tine-mouth' and the 'Sheeldes':

Here I viewed the salt works, wherein is more salt works and more salt made, than in any part of England that I know, and all the salt here is made of salt-water; these pans which are not to be numbered, placed in the river-mouth and wrought with coals brought by water from New-castle pits. A most dainty new salt-work lately here erected, which is absolutely the most complete work I ever saw; in the breadth whereof is placed six rank of pans, four pans in a rank. . . . These twenty four pans have twelve furnaces and twelve fires.

Sir William then went on to describe these works and the pans in detail.

Ninety years later Lord Harley,[15] whilst travelling north, visited South Shields:

. . . which is the chief place for making salt. The houses there are poor little low hovels, and are in a perpetual thick nasty smoke. It has in all 200 salt pans, each employs 3 men. Each pan makes one tun and a $\frac{1}{4}$ of salt at 8 boilings which lasts 3 days and a half. Each consumes 14 chaldrons of coal in 7 days in which time it makes two tuns and a $\frac{1}{2}$ of salt. The wages for Pumpers, ie. those who pump the salt water into the pans is 5d per diem. The watchers ie. those who continually have an eye to the pans and the fire stoves have 6d a day.

A 'Map of County Durham' by Thomas Kitchin of c1750 incorporated an embellishment showing a corner of a salt-pan and a salt-shovel and in addition to this illustration, Kitchin added:

SOUTH SHIELDS, the Station of the Sea Coal Fleets, is a large Village eminent for its Salt Works, here being upwards of 200 Pans for boiling the Sea Water into Salt. 'Tis said that 100,000 Chaldron of Coals are yearly consum'd in these Works.

Equipment for salt making, identical with that illustrated by Thomas Kitchin, may be seen in greater detail in William Brown-rigg's book *The Art of Making Common Salt* (1748). Brine was pumped from the sea at full tide into a brine pit and run from there by lead pipes to each pan. The boiling pans measured about 20ft × 12ft × 14in deep and were built of plates of iron riveted together with iron nails and the joints filled with a cement. Across the top of the pan were placed several strong bars of iron and from these iron hooks hung down to support the pan bottom at intervals. Thus the large area of pan bottom was kept in shape.

A large collection of manuscripts from the Cotesworth family of Durham (fortunately saved from paper pulping in 1940 and now preserved in Gateshead Library), has many references to the eighteenth-century trade in salt and includes an account of 1722 detailing the cost of building a new Pann and Pannhouse. Some of the items (which totalled £145 13s 7½d) were:

| | | | |
|---|---|---|---|
| To 4 boats of hearth stones | 1 | 15 | 6 |
| To Nails | 2 | 3 | 0 |
| To the Pann baulks Makeing | 5 | 0 | 0 |
| To Masons & Labourers at Walls, Hearths | 2 | 16 | 8 |
| To Timbers and Spouts | 15 | 18 | 7 |
| To 4 Koills of Hearth Stones | 8 | 0 | 0 |
| To 13 Pann plates (2¾ tons) | 59 | 2 | 6 |
| To Slabb Iron and flatt Iron | 27 | 4 | 4½ |

Beneath open pans of this description, firegrates and flues boiled the brine and, as this evaporated, salt was skimmed and shovelled off and packed into wicker baskets to drain. Three of these conical baskets can be seen in Kitchin's illustration of 1750.

Despite its considerable success in the seventeenth and eighteenth centuries, the salt trade of the north-east coast declined and at the time that the historian Robert Surtees was writing his *History of Durham* in 1820, he was only able to record five salt-pans still at work in South Shields. The 'panns without number' of a previous century had disappeared.

South Shields was not the only place on the north-east coast to have this thriving industry. Blyth, too, had a reputation for black skies and white salt; and here again all trace has long since gone.[16] Seaton Sluice, that industrial development of the Delaval family, had not only coal workings, glassworks and its own artificial harbour, but a salt works which was large enough in 1779 to pay duty to the Crown of £2,852.[17]

*Notes to this chapter are on page 198.*

# CHAPTER SIX

# *Transport*

## RIVERS

UNTIL the coming of the railway, the three chief rivers of the North East—Tyne, Wear and Tees—were the predominant transport routes.

### *The Tees*

Despite a tortuous route taking many days sailing, ships worked up the Tees as far as Yarm, and visible proof of that river trade still stands in the shape of several large brick-built eighteenth-century granaries, now of course serving other purposes. As ships grew larger and road transport improved, port facilities were developed down-stream at Stockton, for that port and town were growing even before the railway was opened in 1825. The first coal shipments from the Tees were made at Stockton, but the railway company soon began to look for a more convenient shipping point further east and Middles-brough was chosen as the site of a new port by 1830. A town was planned adjoining the new staithes where a 32 acre square was laid out and begun in 1830. Prior to this, the site of Middlesbrough was farmland with four farmhouses. Most of the original town houses of 1830 have fairly recently been demolished, but some of the wooden piles of the old Port Darlington staithes can still be traced and it is near here that the enormous sheer-legs of 1897 stand, powered by steam until electrified in 1966.

### *The Wear*

Further north, and nearer the heart of the old coalfield, the Wear has had a longer history of coal shipment. Although for centuries Newcastle jealously guarded its right to ship coal, by the seventeenth century keels were working on the Wear from almost as far upstream

as Chester-le-Street. Fig 3 shows wagonways down to the Wear in
1787, clustering along the riverside from Fatfield to Washington.
Unlike the Tyne, where collieries and miners' housing mingled with
other industries, the two were separated by geology on the Wear.
Here the staithes, keelmen's cottages and collieries formed an upstream cluster and downstream, near the mouth, was Sunderland,
beginning at North and South Hylton with potteries and boat-
building yards and extending to the sea with shipyards, glassworks,
limekilns and rope walks lining the river. Most of these industries
have gone, but many remains could probably still be found by dili-
gent observation and recording. At the north side of the rivermouth,
in Roker, a small dock was constructed in 1840, and southwards
down the coast from the rivermouth a long line of docks was built
from 1850 to 1856. Here several fine granaries and other dockside
buildings can still be discovered.


*The Tyne*

The river Tyne[1] lies at the heart of the North East and Newcastle
has been the river crossing-point since Roman times. Both up and
downstream from here industry has grown, thrived and waned for
several centuries. It is at once an area rich in industrial archaeology
yet in many parts ruthlessly cleared for new development. It is not
possible in a few paragraphs to describe this complex and absorbing
area, and the most one can do is to sketch the historical development
of the riverside, so that the current remains can be seen in relation to
the whole story.

As early as 1103 settlements along the river were expanding, and
by 1367 coals were being worked at Winlaton and prepared for shipment to Windsor Castle. Newcastle with its geographically advan-
tageous crossing-point quickly grew and dominated the development
of the whole estuary. Small settlements at the Shields (the word
means a temporary building or shelter) are first mentioned in 1259
and their general expansion with salt works, wharves, breweries and

salmon fishing was seen as a threat to the upstream port and an
infringement of the rights of the freemen of Newcastle. In the fourteenth century the triangular battle between the Bishop of Durham,
the City of Newcastle and the Prior of Tynemouth over development
and export trades came to a head. Newcastle lodged a petition with
Edward III complaining that:

> . . . the Prior of Tynemouth has raised a town on the bank of the water
> at Sheles on the one side of the water and that the Prior of Durham has
> raised another town on the other side of the water, where no towns ought
> to be but only huts for sheltering fishermen and that fishermen sold fish
> there which ought to be sold at Newcastle, to the great injury of the
> whole Borough, and in detriment of the tolls of our Lord and King at the
> Castle.

The king gave his agreement in 1303 in favour of Newcastle, whereby
South Shields and Tynemouth were forbidden to hold fairs or markets, ships coming to the Tyne were to be loaded and unloaded only
at Newcastle and all wrecks of sea and river (there were 9 miles of
shoals and sandbars) were to fall to the king.

This favoured position of Newcastle remained until around 1850,
though by the eighteenth century the twin settlements of the Shields
were beginning to overcome this legal obstacle. It was economic and
not political circumstances which led to the gradual relaxation of the
prohibitory laws of Newcastle, for as the coal trade grew and the size
of the vessels increased, loading and storing of coal and repairing of
vessels had to be done nearer the sea.

The pattern of industrial development on Tyneside can be seen as
several overlapping phases:

| | |
|---|---|
| Up to the 15th century | Agricultural river traffic: wool, hides and grain |
| 13th century onwards | The coal trade |
| 17th century onwards | Glass manufacture and early chemical industry |
| 17th and 18th centuries | Salt works |
| 17th century onwards | Iron smelting |
| 19th century onwards | Manufacture of locomotives, iron, ships and machinery |

A significant date for the North East was the Act of Union with Scotland in 1707, for this brought general security to the Border region and encouraged quay extension beyond the town walls of Newcastle. The running of wagonways from the colliery right down to the river edge led to the development of special docking facilities: the coal staithes which have already been described (p 43). By the eighteenth century there were also two other distinct types of quay facility: ballast quays and cargo-handling quays, and by 1760 ballast hills (where ballast sand brought by unladen vessels was tipped) extended as far downstream from Newcastle as Jarrow.

The nineteenth century was the period when the greatest social, physical and economic changes took place on Tyneside. Up till 1810 the Spanish Battery, near the mouth of the Tyne, was in constant action dealing with French privateers and men-of-war and the coal fleets were constantly under attack. In 1803 an iron chain, made specially at Swalwell, was laid across the Tynemouth Bar nightly as a safeguard against the night entry of French fireships at the time of the expected invasion. But the end of the Napoleonic Wars marked the last phase of insecurity prior to the great economic depression of the 1930s. Later in the century the riverside became transformed into the industrialised complex with which we are familiar today. Major industrial concerns such as the Walker Iron Works fronted the river on the Newcastle shore, and across the river ironworks, alkali works, glassworks and shipyards occupied the bank.

By Act of Parliament in 1850 the Tyne Improvement Commission was set up, with the task of making the Tyne a deep and easily navigable river and subsequently maintaining it in this condition. Piers were built at the mouth of the river, a channel dredged upstream, projecting points such as Whitehill Point and Bill Point cut back, South Shields harbour cleared of shoals and the old quarry at Newcastle almost wholly rebuilt and provided with warehouses and cranes. The old stone bridge at Newcastle was demolished and the Swing Bridge erected in its place. Northumberland Dock, an important coaling point was opened in 1857 and in 1859 the North Eastern

Railway Company opened Tyne Dock on a part of Jarrow Slake. Here coal was loaded from West and Central Durham by way of the Pontop & South Shields Railway. Albert Edward Dock was opened in 1854.

Though the Tyne has a shipbuilding tradition extending back to medieval times, the present great tradition really dates from the 1840s, when the first iron ship was launched at Walker. The ever-growing size of ships, balanced in part by the deepening and widening of the river, led to the construction of the Palmer dock-yards at Hebburn and Jarrow and the Walker, Wallsend and Elswick shipyards. In effect, shipbuilding in the 1870s was concentrated on the 5 mile stretch of the Tyne between Bill Point and Albert Dock entrance, and ship repairers and fitters were to be found in the vicinity of North and South Shields.

Whilst the nineteenth century created the general pattern of Tyne-side, the twentieth century has generally made little fundamental change. Thus for instance there has been no major port development on the scale of Tyne Dock, though specialised quayage for coal ship-ment at Harton, oil storage at Jarrow, and iron-ore quays at Tyne Dock have been built. The once notable Northumberland Dock is now semi-derelict and little-used and Tyne Dock, which no more than thirty years ago was filled with colliers loading at four large timber staithes, is quite changed and the staithes have been cut down to water level. The 'Arches' (p 122) alone remain to remind the road user of this recent coal traffic (Plate, p 18), for the coal-carrying railways ran over the road here and on to the staithes in the Dock (Fig 22).

PORTS

The ports of the North East have naturally echoed, in their exports, the mineral wealth of the interior. Seahouses and Beadnell, as men-tioned in the previous chapter, have exported lime due to their unique position. Craster has exported whinstone. From Amble southwards—Blyth, Shields, Sunderland and Seaham—coal has been the chief, and in several cases practically the only, export. At the very south of the region, Port Mulgrave exported iron ore which was shipped to the Tyne for processing.

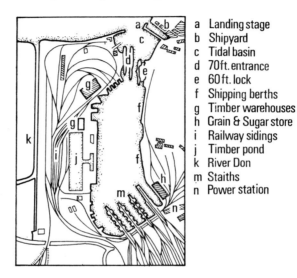

a  Landing stage
b  Shipyard
c  Tidal basin
d  70ft. entrance
e  60ft. lock
f  Shipping berths
g  Timber warehouses
h  Grain & Sugar store
i  Railway sidings
j  Timber pond
k  River Don
m  Staiths
n  Power station

22    Plan of Tyne Dock, near South Shields, c1930. The staithes are now dismantled, though the Arches by which the wagonways crossed the road still stand

While some of these ports were designed and built specifically to handle the inland mineral resources, others would have existed had there never been minerals. Berwick-on-Tweed, a natural port, served an otherwise isolated area and until the coming of the railway was of much greater local importance. Large warehouses can still be traced by the riverside, some semi-derelict, others converted to later uses. Shipbuilding has now dwindled and the export of salmon (fished from the Tweed) is greatly diminished. One unusual export, eggs, for which the area was famous in the late-eighteenth and early-nineteenth centuries, has now ceased.[2]

Seahouses and Beadnell are good examples of small fishing villages which must, around 1800, have been busy little industrial ports, but which have now reverted to very slight local use. Craster also has returned largely to local use; though here the small industry of kippering has kept its name famous over a wide area. Alnmouth is a rather sad place: in the fifteenth century a port for Alnwick, in the nineteenth century flourishing upon the import of guano and export of grain, it is today a small holiday resort with crumbling warehouses and traces of the harbour, now completely silted-up. Amble too has shrunk and the coal industry is gradually withdrawing further south.

There are, in the region, three good examples of ports which have been artificially constructed on an otherwise unsuitable coastline in order to export minerals: Seaton Sluice in Northumberland, Seaham Harbour in Durham and Port Mulgrave in Yorkshire. The two northerly ones have been largely carved out of the rock and the most southerly one was built into the sea. Of these only Seaham Harbour continues to operate and that somewhat precariously.

The most northerly, earliest, and possibly the most dramatic of the three is Seaton Sluice, built between 1761 and 1764 by Thomas Delavel, industrialist and coal-owner.[3] The slight natural harbour at the mouth of the Seaton Burn had served in the late-seventeenth century, but was very shallow and hence the new cut was made to the east (Fig 23). Dock gates at each end, built of timber baulks sliding in grooves in the rock, provided an additional entrance to the old harbour and also a deep-water dock where vessels could be loaded by spouts or cranes at all states of tide. The cut, 800ft long, 30ft wide × 52ft deep took three years to make and cost £10,000. An interesting feature was the cutting-out of the stone which was carefully extracted in suitable blocks and used for nearby building. A pier was built out to protect the entrance and on 20 March 1764 two vessels sailed in though the sea was high and the wind easterly. On 22 March the *Warkworth* sailed out with 273 tons of coal aboard. Some measure of the early success of this port may be seen from the fact that in 1777, as many as 177 vessels loaded a total of almost 48,000 tons of coal for London. Yet coal was not the only export, for in 1763 Delavel had founded a glassworks and the products of this were also exported. Most of the materials for glass production were on hand locally, but ashes and pot-clay were imported and made useful ballast for the incoming ships. For almost a hundred years the port operated despite great difficulties but with the development of the steam-coal district of Northumberland in the 1840s, the deficiencies of Seaton Sluice became more obvious. Agitation for better shipping accommodation led to the construction of the Northumberland Dock on the Tyne and to the improvement of Blyth. The appalling disaster at New Hartley Colliery in 1862, when the beam of a pumping engine fell down the shaft, trapping 204 men and boys, was the final blow and shortly afterwards the port ceased to operate. The bottle works closed in 1870 and the glasshouse cones were demolished twenty-five years later to make way for houses.

While Seaton Sluice grew from an earlier, though small, harbour enlarged in the eighteenth century, Seaham Harbour had no predecessor. No port had ever existed here; there was no natural harbour of any sort. Credit for the idea of a coal-shipping port goes to Sir Ralph Noel who, in 1820, instructed an engineer named William Chapman to prepare a plan by which some of the inlets on the coast might be expanded and piers built on the rocks for their shelter.[4] Shortly afterwards the Marquis of Londonderry purchased the estates and directed Mr Chapman to prepare a more ambitious design. Lord Londonderry required an outlet for his extensive collieries in the Hutton Seam district to the south of Sunderland, and at that time the port of Sunderland was too small for such large shipments. Work began on 28 November 1828 when the marquis performed a stone-laying ceremony at the north pier. Later that day the young Viscount Seaham, who was almost eight years old, laid the foundation stone for the first house of Seaham town. The town, designed by the architect John Dobson (responsible for much fine building in Newcastle), was thus planned along with the harbour and the two grew together.

The Seaham outer harbour, formed by piers, was so constructed

Page 125 (above) The Transporter Bridge at Middlesbrough. Built in 1911, this is one of two remaining transporter bridges (the other is at Newport, Mon); (right) large sheer-legs (1897) at Middlesbrough. These were constructed for lifting-in ships' boilers, when shipbuilding flourished here. They were converted from steam to electricity in 1966

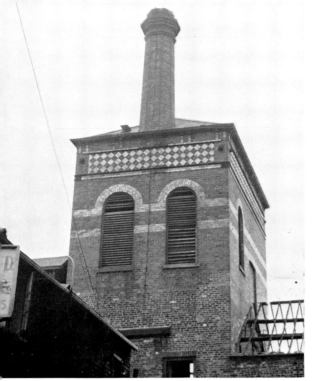

Page 126 (left) *Castle Brewery at Stockton, recently demolished*; (below) *old brewery at Houghton-le-Spring. Long out of use as a brewery and now standing empty*

not only to protect the initial docks, but also all future extensions which could be foreseen. A north and middle dock were excavated, together with a small south dry-dock, with a shipbuilding yard at its southern extremity. Around the inner harbour, on the cliffs, were hauling machinery, coal drops, offices, workshops and timber yards, etc. The first coal was shipped in 1831 and in 1905 the original middle dock was enlarged towards the south, incorporating and extending beyond the earlier dry-dock. This, now known as South Dock, is the present centre of coal shipments and North Dock is used only by local fishermen. The gates to the North Dock were powered by a beam engine and when this was taken out of use some years ago part of the engine was taken into store by Gateshead Museum and has now been passed to the Regional Open Air Museum. The gates to the South Dock are now powered by hydraulic rams and the pumping machinery is housed at the north-west corner of the dock.

Seaton Sluice and Seaham Harbour were excavated from the solid rock, but Port Mulgrave on the North Yorkshire coast was built out into the sea.[5] Originally called Rosedale Docks, the two stone-built jetties which enclosed an area of about 3 acres were constructed in the early 1850s for the shipment of ironstone. At that time Messrs Palmers of Jarrow-on-Tyne acquired a lease for working ironstone in the area and commenced mining the top seam of ironstone, some 200ft up the cliff face. Originally the stone was lowered to the jetty by a self-acting inclined plane, but this was followed by sinking a shaft back from the cliff, to a depth of about 22 fathoms, and connecting this by a short tunnel to the dock. The tunnel or drift entrance is 25–30ft above sea level, so the stone was run in tubs along a 3ft gauge railway built on a large wooden gantry erected on the southern arm of the stone jetty. A series of 20 wooden boxes was built into this gantry, as bunkers to store the ironstone, each box holding 50 or 60 tons. Loading a vessel was accomplished quickly, so that a ship entering during high tide could leave harbour before low water.

In 1874 Palmers obtained further ironstone royalties in the nearby

H

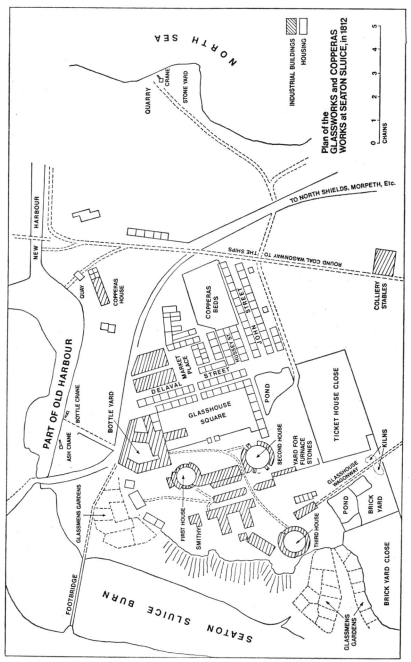

23  Plan of Seaton Sluice, 1812. (Based on a very detailed plan in the Northumberland County Record Office)

valley of Grinkle and the main drift at Port Mulgrave was extended through the hillside, making a tunnel a mile long and connecting the dock, by the 3ft gauge railway line, with the Grinkle Mine 2½ miles away. By 1880 the Port Mulgrave workings were exhausted, but Grinkle stone continued to be shipped until 1916 when a steep incline was constructed in the valley at Grinkle, leading up to the main NER line from Loftus to Whitby. Now little remains of Port Mulgrave: its jetties are being broken by the heavy seas and only a few cottages remain on this once-more lonely stretch of coast.

Finally mention should be made of what is probably the oldest remaining lighthouse on the north-east coast, at Blyth. There have been others, replaced by later structures, but this, built in 1788 by Sir Matthew Ridley as a guiding light for ships entering the estuary, still stands in a back street and is now appropriately used as the headquarters of the Northumberland Yacht Club.

## CANALS

Looked at in one way, transport by water has played a predominant part in the history of the North East, yet from another point of view water transport has been practically unrepresented in the region. The viewpoint varies according to whether one is interested in river and sea transport, or in canal history.

The canal historian will be able to trace occasional attempts to promote canals, for instance those that preceded the Stockton & Darlington Railway (p 135), but only one canal system was actually constructed in our area: that from the river Swale to Bedale in Yorkshire in about 1770, and even there it seems doubtful whether the canal ever carried goods commercially.

Since the Middle Ages, York had stood at the centre of an inland navigation system linking the rivers Ouse, Swale, Ure, Wharfe and Derwent and attempts were made in the eighteenth century to modernise and extend this system. An Act of 1767[6] authorised the Swale being made navigable from its junction with the rivers Ure and

Ouse, to Morton Bridge, together with a proposed navigation of Bedale Beck. A subsequent Act of 1770 made a number of alterations to the scheme and a Company of Proprietors was set up with powers to raise £30,000. One of the difficulties in the way of making the Swale navigable was Topcliffe Mill, and John Smeaton was called in to advise on the removal of the mill to a new site. Yet within a very short time of the start of the construction, the Ouse Commissioners were told in 1787 that Linton Lock was collapsing, leading one to suppose that little traffic got beyond it on to the Swale at this period. Linton Lock, which was 8 miles south-east of Boroughbridge (SE 500601), was built to allow boats 60ft long × 15ft 4in wide with a 4ft draught, and measurements of the lock at Leeming, Yorkshire, indicate that boats of that size would also have been able to pass this part of the navigation (Fig 24).[7]

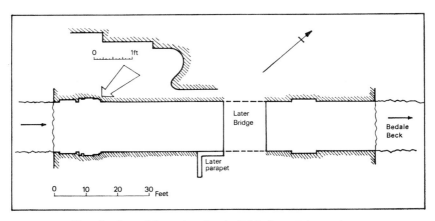

24    Sketch-plan of Leeming Lock. This late eighteenth-century lock and the basin at Bedale are the only true canal remains in the region

Within the North East, the only visible remains of this Yorkshire system are at Leeming where the small lock is visible from the North Road (A1) south-bound carriageway and at Bedale where part of the masonry of a basin remains, together with several mooring rings. Further south, and really out of our area, an old warehouse and wharf can be traced at Thirsk and nearby a Methodist chapel stands on another wharf, the masonry of which still contains mooring rings.

Whilst the Bedale Beck navigation was the only lengthy canal system in the North East, commercially more important works were the Mandale and Portrack Cuts, of 1810 and 1831 respectively, on the river Tees. From Stockton the Tees formerly reached its estuary by way of two enormous meanders. The first, the Mandale loop, began half a mile below Stockton and looped to the south for $2\frac{1}{2}$ miles before returning to within a furlong of where it began. The course of this loop can still be traced and is the site of the Mandale Marshes and present race course. The second and shorter loop continued northward around Portrack.

Credit for first proposing, in 1769, a cut to avoid the Mandale loop is given to Edmund Harvey, a pewterer of Stockton. Nothing came of the scheme in his lifetime but the name Harvey's cut seems to have persisted for many years and despite opposition from Lord Harewood who owned a mill and land around Mandale, the scheme was at last begun in 1809 and finished in September 1810. Its length was a mere 154yd.[8]

This first cut having proved an unqualified success, the second or Portrack Cut was begun in June 1829 and, being longer than its predecessor (725yd), was not finished until February 1831. Fig 25 illustrates the position of these two cuts which finally shortened the journey from Stockton to Teesmouth by more than three miles.

## ROADS AND BRIDGES

Sometimes looked upon as a 'fringe' concern of the industrial archaeologist, road systems and their bridges are nevertheless an an essential part of the industrial complex of a region and are today as subject to change as any other part.

As we have seen, the northern counties were largely unaffected by canal construction, but by 1800 great improvements in the roads and bridges had taken place. The main roads, including the Great North Road, had been turnpiked about the middle of the eighteenth century,

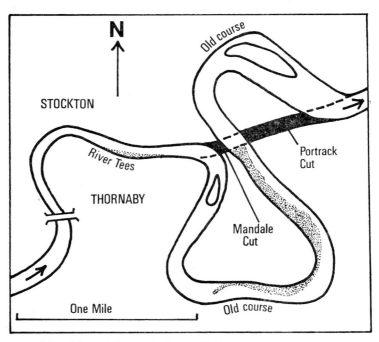

25    Mandale and Portrack Cuts, Middlesbrough. These two cuts (1810 and 1831) shortened the river journey from Stockton to Tees Mouth by about three miles

and the second half of that century witnessed a general improvement of the roads. It was not until the 1820s however, that new turnpike roads penetrated the lead-mining dales and, whereas the coal-mining areas had long been served by wagonways, transport of lead ore from mines to smelting mills and of the lead from there to the ports was still by panniers hung across the backs of dales ponies or Galloways.[9] Surprisingly few turnpike tollhouses survive: one small example stands at the west end of the (rebuilt) bridge at Ponteland. A small building, near Egglestone, known locally as the 'saddle-house' and on the route down from the Egglestone lead smelt-mills to Barnard Castle and thence to the coast, is a direct link with the pack-horse era (p 73).

Yet if tollhouses and milestones are scarce, there are some fine bridges, though one of the earliest suspension bridges, the Scotswood Bridge of 1829, has recently been demolished. This, designed by Sir Samuel Brown, was an elaboration of his earlier magnificent Union Chain Bridge across the Tweed at Loan End, of 1820. Fortunately this latter stands on a little-used road and is probably secure for a few more years. It is now Britain's earliest surviving suspension bridge, although an interesting footway suspension bridge over the Tees, the Winch Bridge at Holwick, has a longer history and it seems likely that there was a chain suspension bridge at this point in the mid-eighteenth century.

The region has several fine medieval and seventeenth-century stone bridges, for example Durham, Elvet, twelfth century; Durham, Framwellgate, c1400; Yarm, c1400; Catterick, 1425; Twizell, fifteenth century; Berwick-on-Tweed, 1610; Corbridge, 1674. Many old bridges were swept away in the great storm of 1771 and this fact, together with turnpike construction in the eighteenth century, explains why so many fine bridges of the late-eighteenth century are to be found, such as Chollerford, 1775; Hexham, 1785; Ridley Hall, 1789; Lintzford, late-eighteenth century; Greta Bridge, 1789.

Turning to the nineteenth century, in addition to the suspension bridges already mentioned, there are several interesting examples of engineering such as the Swing Bridge at Newcastle upon Tyne of 1876. This is built on the line of all the earlier Newcastle bridges: Roman, thirteenth-century, and eighteenth-century. The last, built by Robert Mylne in 1772–9 had to make way for a bridge which would allow higher vessels to pass upstream. The Swing Bridge, beneath which two ribbed arches of one of the earlier bridges are visible, was until recently powered by hydraulic engines supplied by

W. G. Armstrong. There are several fine railway bridges and viaducts, from Berwick-on-Tweed to Yarm, but these are referred to when railways are considered later in this chapter.

Finally, mention should be made of two curious Middlesbrough bridges: the Transporter Bridge of 1911 and the Newport Bridge of 1934. The former comprises a platform or car (recently enlarged) which carries vehicles and pedestrians and is drawn across the river suspended by cables from an overhead trolley.[10] Only one other similar bridge operates in the British Isles—at Newport, Monmouthshire. The other Middlesbrough bridge is a clumsy-looking structure which was designed to lift the roadway complete, for the passage of vessels, but which is now rarely raised. Its importance lies in the link which it provides between Middlesbrough and County Durham and, as Teesside and the new county of Cleveland develop, its importance will continue to grow.

## RAILWAYS[11]

In common with most historical development, the railway system of the North East has grown irregularly and without any planning. We can thus find lines running along routes which were laid down more than two centuries ago for quite a different purpose, and in other places disused routes (some never even completed) can be traced for many miles. It is clearly not possible to synthesise such a complex and interwoven history into a few pages. If one were to take as an example merely the history of actual and proposed rail services around the City of Durham one would find the task a lengthy one, for there were many attempts and promises of attempts to bring a line and station to that city and such a detailed story would be out of place here. The reader wishing to know more is referred to the regional history *Railways of North East England* by K. Hoole (1965), and to the original and thorough history *The North Eastern Railway* by W. W. Tomlinson (1914).

Instead of wearying the reader with dates and routes, an attempt is made here to sketch some of the more significant events which led to the gradual evolution of the North Eastern Railway system and to fit into this history the few early sites which still remain on the ground.

## The Stockton & Darlington Railway

The line from which it may fairly be said all subsequent public railways sprang was that of the Stockton & Darlington Railway, and the story of that line goes back as far as 1768, thirteen years before George Stephenson was born. While the Tyne coalfield was successfully developing due to its proximity to water transport, the smaller Auckland coalfield in south-west Durham was seriously handicapped by the long overland journey to Stockton, where the Tees became effectively navigable. From time to time attempts were made locally to remedy this situation and in 1768 a canal route was surveyed, by James Brindley's son-in-law Robert Whitworth, from Stockton to Winston Bridge near Barnard Castle, with branches to Yarm, Croft and Piercebridge. Brindley himself went over the line and confirmed the proposed route and estimated costs. Nothing came of this nor of subsequent revisions and similar schemes in the late-eighteenth century. The first practical river improvement came when the Mandale Cut was made on the Tees near Stockton, and completed in 1810 (p 131).

At a dinner at Stockton Town Hall to celebrate this new cut, the question of communications from the Auckland coalfield was not unnaturally raised again. This time however the canal enthusiasts found themselves facing, for the first time, those who favoured a horse tramway, led especially by the local Quaker banker Edward Pease. As a result a committee was set up to investigate the matter and, after various vicissitudes, George Overton was brought in from Breconshire in 1818 to survey a route for a horse tramroad.

It may seem surprising, when one remembers the extensive wooden wagonways of Tyneside, that the Stockton & Darlington promoters should go so far as Breconshire for their engineer, but it must be remembered that South Wales was the cradle of cast-iron tramways and George Overton was an engineer with great experience of constructing and operating them. He had, for example, built the Pen-y-Daren tramway on which Trevithick's locomotive made its first epic journey.

On the very day (1821) that the s & DR Act based on Overton's survey was passed, George Stephenson first met Edward Pease. It seems to have been an unfortunate habit of canal (and later railway) promoters to seek advice from every engineer they thought could assist them and the conflicting advice and jealousies so engendered did little to help them forward. On this occasion Stephenson seems to have convinced Pease that steam traction on edge rails was preferable to a horse tramway or plateway and from that moment George Overton is no longer in evidence. Stephenson was invited to re-survey the line and the new Act which authorised his major deviations from Overton's line received the royal assent in 1823.

This historic line, opened on 27 September 1825, has a number of 'firsts' to its credit. A technical development of considerable significance was John Birkinshaw's patent of 1821, referring to a method of rolling wrought-iron rails of 'I' section. Until this date the only alternative to cast-iron rails had been simple square-section wrought-iron bars. Stephenson seized on this idea, disregarding his own pecuniary interest in the Stephenson & Losh cast-iron rails; not unnaturally this quickly brought to an end his association with Messrs Losh, Wilson & Bell. But the Bedlington Ironworks, where the Birkinshaw rails were being made, was not equipped to construct the locomotives and stationary engines of Stephenson's design which had previously been built by Losh, Wilson & Bell at the Walker Ironworks. It was this situation which led directly to the founding of the famous firm of Robert Stephenson & Company in Newcastle.

Another historic feature of the s & DR was the company's decision to engage an architect: the first railway in the world to do so. This architect was Ignatius Bonomi of Durham, elder son of the celebrated eighteenth-century architect Joseph Bonomi. He it was who designed the Skerne Bridge at Darlington, a handsome bridge now almost concealed by the adjacent gas works, but which figures prominently in the famous painting of the opening procession by John Dobbin. A small farm-access bridge at the foot of the Brusselton West incline is obviously also based on that same design and is quite attractive despite its local and mundane function.

The most notable and historic feature of the line is too well-known to stress, namely the use of steam locomotives. Two points should however be made clear. Steam locomotives had been in use on other lines for colliery haulage for several years, but the s & DR was the first public line in the world to employ locomotives. Yet the railway also incorporated stationary haulage engines, these being at the western end of the line at Etherley and Brusselton, to the west and east of West Auckland respectively.

One more 'first' was the construction of the world's first iron railway bridge, the famous bridge over the river Gaunless between the two inclines. Fortunately this bridge now stands preserved in the National Transport Collection, York, and the stone abutments can still be traced along the river bank.

The western section of this famous line makes a pleasant walk for the industrial archaeologist and illustrates something of the technical problems and achievements of the first great railway builder, as well as the economic and geographical background to the process by which the railway revolution was inaugurated. One may begin walking from Low Etherley, following the track up Etherley Incline, down to West Auckland, past the site of the Gaunless Bridge, up towards Brusselton Bank where one passes the attractive little farm-access bridge already mentioned and the old stationary-engine house at the bank top now converted to a cottage, and so down to Shildon. It is rather unfortunate that this historic route is not yet marked as such on our one-inch Ordnance Survey maps.

On the map of the original s & DR route (Fig 26) will be seen the position of those features which are mostly still standing and more detailed information about these will be found in the Gazetteer.

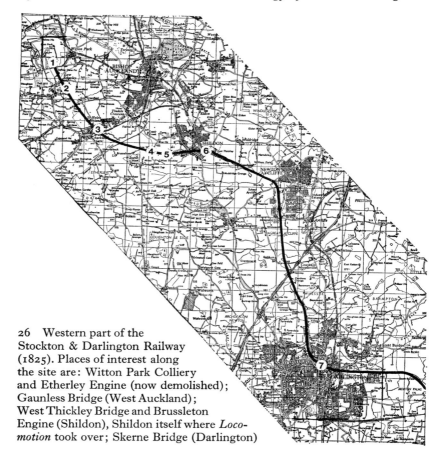

26   Western part of the
Stockton & Darlington Railway
(1825). Places of interest along
the site are: Witton Park Colliery
and Etherley Engine (now demolished);
Gaunless Bridge (West Auckland);
West Thickley Bridge and Brussleton
Engine (Shildon), Shildon itself where *Locomotion* took over; Skerne Bridge (Darlington)

## *The Stanhope & Tyne Railway*

The story of this railway is an exciting one for not only did it run
up steep hills, cut across many miles of bleak moorland and negotiate
a deep gorge, but it almost caused Robert Stephenson's bankruptcy.
Today its route is still a pleasure to traverse and several of its ruined
buildings are worth seeking out.

There is limestone at Stanhope in Weardale and in 1831 a scheme was launched to build a lime works there and join this by rail to a colliery at Medomsley near Consett in the Derwent Valley. It was at first proposed that this should be linked with the old Pontop and Tanfield colliery wagonways which provided a route to the Tyne, but this idea was dropped in favour of a completely new line. This ambitious new scheme was to carry the line twenty-four miles further east[12] to reach the Tyne below the bridge, where larger vessels could be used. Crushed limestone was of course in growing demand as a blast-furnace flux and, as the railway revolution was increasing the demand for iron, the prospectus for the Stanhope & Tyne Railway looked promising on paper.

The line was surveyed by T. E. Harrison, and Robert Stephenson (son of George Stephenson the pioneer engineer of the Stockton & Darlington Railway) agreed to act as consulting engineer. Unfortunately Stephenson allowed himself to be persuaded to accept five £100 shares in the company's stock in lieu of his agreed fee of £1,000, and this he regretted a few years later.

### *Stanhope & Tyne Railway (1834)*

Numbers refer to the map (Fig 27)

| *From* | *Motive power* | *By Gradient* | *Distance* |
|---|---|---|---|
| 1 Stanhope Kilns (796ft OD) | Engine | (up) 1 in 12 <br> 1 in 8 | ½m |
| 2 Crawley Engine | Engine | (up) 1 in 21 <br> 1 in 13 | 1m |
| 3 Weatherhill Engine | Horse | 1 in 2,059 <br> 1 in 80 | ½m <br> 1m |
| 4 Park Head wheelhouse | Engine (tail rope) | 1 in 80 | 1½m |

| From | Motive power | By Gradient | Distance |
|---|---|---|---|
| 5  Meeting Slacks Engine | Engine | 1 in 40 approx | 1¼m |
| 6  Top of Nanny Mayor's Bank (Waskerley) | SA incline | 1 in 14 | ¾m |
| 7  Foot of Bank | Horse | 1 in 680 | 1¼m |
| 8  Healeyfield Bridge | Free (horse in dandy cart) | 1 in 132 | 2m |
| 9  Hownes Gill Engine (and later viaduct) | Engine at foot of ravine | 160ft deep | 800ft wide |
|  | Engine | (up) 1 in 71 | 1¼m |
| 10  Carr House Engine | Engine | 1 in 108 | ¾m |
| 11  East Carr House | Horse | NS | 2¼m |
| 12  Bantling Castle | Engine | (up) NS | 662yd |
| 13  Annfield Engine | Engine | NS | 1,056yd |
| 14  Foot of 'Loud Bank'; beginning of Stanley Level | Horse | NS | 2½m |
| 15  West Stanley: head of Stanley Bank | SA incline | 1 in 21 | 1,276yd |
| 16  Head of Twizell Bank | SA incline | 1 in 17½ | 880yd |
| 17  Head of Eden Hill Bank | SA incline | 1 in 17 1 in 70 | 1,122yd |
| 18  West end of Pelton Level | Horse | NS | 1,331yd |
| 19  Head of Waldridge Bank | SA incline | 1 in 20½ | 1¼m |
| 20  Stella Gill | Engine (tail rope) | almost level | ¾m |

| From | Motive power | By Gradient | Distance |
|---|---|---|---|
| 21 High Flatts Engine | Engine | NS | ¾m |
| 22 Durham turnpike-road | Horse | (up) | ¾m |
| 23 Vigo Engines (double) | Engine | NS | 1m |
| 24 Worked from here to South Shields by locomotive | Locomotive | Fall of 12ft  Fall of 69½ft | 5m  4¼m |

|  | Total miles |
|---|---|
| Horses | 10½ |
| Self-acting inclines | 3 |
| Stationary engines (9 totalling 375hp) | 11 |
| Locomotives | 9¼ |
|  | 33¾ |

*Notes:*
(up) on *gradient* refers to direction *from* Stanhope
SA incline = self-acting incline (ie loaded trucks descended by gravity
and returned the empty trucks)
NS = figures not stated (other figures are based on W. W. Tomlinson,
*The North Eastern Railway*, 1914)

The route was a formidable one, but in the early days of railway engineering it was looked upon more as a challenge than as an unwise project. When completed in 1834 the S & TR combined every form of motive power then known. Ten and a half miles were worked by horses, 9 stationary engines hauled on a total of 11 miles, there were 5 self-acting inclines totalling 3 miles and 9¼ miles were worked by locomotives. In addition the daunting Hownes Gill ravine was negotiated by the following remarkable device. A single fixed engine at the foot of the gorge worked a steep incline up each side, the gradients being 1 in 3 and 1 in 2½. The wagons were run on to special incline-carriages which ran on two sets of rails, the outer ones being of 7ft gauge. The fixed engine worked both inclines simultaneously, so helping to balance its load, but even so it could not pass more than twelve wagons in an hour. This obstacle was eventually overcome, in 1858, by a fine twelve-arch viaduct 750ft long and 150ft high built of bricks from Pease's firebrick works near Crook.

The physical difficulties of the line, daunting though they were, might have been satisfactorily overcome had the financial arrangements been sound. But such was not the case, and the rash speculation and lack of commercial wisdom seem incredible in retrospect. Instead of applying to Parliament for an Act of Incorporation, the company proceeded by obtaining wayleaves from the landowners over whose land the railway would pass. This was, of course, the way in which for centuries the wagonways of Tyneside had been constructed, and was therefore not in itself an innovation. Indeed wayleaves across the moor from Stanhope were obtained very cheaply but, when the decision was made to extend the line to South Shields, the company found itself at the mercy of the landowners who held it to ransom for high-rental wayleaves. This resulted in the company being financially stretched long before it obtained any financial return. The line was opened in 1841, but further mismanagement led to the company becoming insolvent and being dissolved in that same year; Robert Stephenson, as a shareholder, found himself jointly responsible for its staggering debts. Having so lately won success and prosperity as a civil engineer he suddenly found himself facing, through no fault of his own, the prospect of utter financial ruin. Realising that only by his own action could he avoid his downfall, he called an extraordinary meeting of the S & TR shareholders on 29 December 1840. Subsequently, after selling half his interest in Robert Stephenson & Co, which was primarily concerned with locomotive building, he set about forming a new company; the Pontop & South Shields, and happily succeeded in preventing further losses.

In 1844 the safety of shareholders was finally ensured when the eastern part of the line (north-east of Washington) was incorporated in the Darlington–Tyne rail link sponsored by the railway king George

Page 143 (left)
*Ullathorne's Mill at Startforth. Near the river crossing to Barnard Castle, this fine late eighteenth-century linen-spinning mill is deserted and threatened with demolition;*
*(right) Dewars Lane granary at Berwick-on-Tweed. Many attractive old granaries and warehouses can be found in this small town*

Page 144 (above) *A farm with a chimney near Berwick-on-Tweed. Buttery Hall Farm (see also Fig 34) had a mid-nineteenth-century thresher powered by a stationary steam engine;* (below) *eighteenth-century lime kilns at Beadnell. Lime was exported down the coast from the small harbour adjoining this attractive group of kilns*

Hudson. This slightly dubious action has been a cause of criticism, but it must be remembered that Robert Stephenson was under powerful pressure to safeguard his interests so nearly destroyed by the Stanhope & Tyne downfall.

When the new Pontop & South Shields Railway Company took over the eastern part of the old Stanhope & Tyne track, the western section was sold to the Derwent Iron Company to transport limestone from the Crawleyside quarries at Stanhope to its furnaces at Consett. Later in 1845, this passed into the hands of the Stockton & Darlington Railway. It can now be seen why S & DR boundary stones can be found along the Weatherhill incline and why an S & DR cottage (bearing the identification plaque K 1), is to be seen in the Crawleyside quarry. This change of ownership probably also accounts for the two types of lime kiln to be seen in the quarry and which are dealt with at more length on p 106.

Fig 27 illustrates the route of the original S & TR and on it are marked the positions of those buildings or structures which still remain. Further reference to these sites will be found in the Gazetteer.

*Other railways*

A study of the complex railway history of the North East is not helped by the prevalence of coal companies which ran their own lines, many of which remained private until the nationalisation of the coal industry, and today the National Coal Board owns and operates many miles of railway line. A multiplicity of small railway companies trading under such colourful names as Brandling Junction, Dearness Valley, Hexham & Allendale or Merrybent & Darlington were gradually amalgamated. In 1854 the North Eastern Railway was formed from four constituent companies operating from York and in the North East. In 1863 the Stockton & Darlington Railway, which by then extended across County Durham and into Westmorland and Yorkshire, formally became part of it, although for a further ten years it carried on almost as a separate concern with its own secretary,

I

solicitor, officers and servants, and fixing the times and details of its own trains.

## *Typical railway features*

The special character of the several companies, and especially of the s & DR, can still be traced by the industrial archaeologist. Such

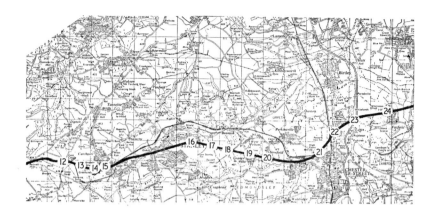

27   Western part of the Stanhope & Tyne Railway (1834). (The
numbers refer to the chart on pp 139–41)

buildings as Durham Gilesgate goods station, Monkwearmouth
station and also Newcastle Central station are good examples of a
regional style, now rapidly being destroyed. Other less obvious
buildings, serving mundane purposes such as coal cells, goods sheds,
engine sheds, etc, also retain a regional character; they are all worthy
of adequate recording. It is somewhat surprising, when one considers
the great numbers of railway-history enthusiasts, to find that such
buildings rarely come within their notice. A few examples of goods
sheds worth seeing are: Belford, a large well-built two-track shed;
Chathill, a similar building but now lacking a roof; and Winston, a
small single-track stone-built shed with its original wooden crane
still in position. At least one water-tank still stands: at Belford, by
Richardson & Sons of Castle Eden (1848). There are simple open,
typical NER coal cells at Winston and a good pair at Waskerley. Also
at Waskerley is a weigh-bridge by H. Pooley & Son of Birmingham
(1910), and another of 1914 by the same maker at Frosterley.

One interesting and individualistic feature of the Stockton & Darlington Railway was its systematic numbering of railway houses. These were identified by letters signifying areas and by serial numbers within each area. Thus F 10 is to be seen on a house near the now disused Barnard Castle station, and K 1 is on the small cottage at Crawleyside quarry (see Stanhope in Gazetteer), whilst K 8 is on the old station house at Waskerley. Each letter and number was set up in a black and white ceramic tile built into the upper wall of the house. A few of these have unfortunately been stolen by unscrupulous collectors, but many remain. Appendix 3 lists all the remaining plaques.

North Eastern Railway characteristics are not all so small or insignificant. There are fine viaducts such as the Victoria Viaduct (1838) near Washington and that at Yarm of 1849 which has, on the river pier, what must surely be the largest stone inscription ever built on a railway viaduct (see p 331 in Gazetteer). There are many bridges, small and large, ranging from a plain metal bridge over the A1 to the south-east of Alnwick inscribed 'Robt Stephenson & Co. 1848'[13] to the fine High Level Bridge which Stephenson put across the Tyne in 1845–9, combining road and rail in a structure which at any rate on the lower road section is carrying a load many many times greater than can ever have been envisaged by its builder.

Finally some mention must be made of locomotives and rolling stock. *Locomotion*, No 1 of the s & DR, is too well known to miss on Darlington station but, as so often has happened in recent industrial history, none of the 'second generation' locomotives have been preserved. Fortunately it has proved possible, after a struggle, to preserve a type J 21 locomotive (NER Type C 1, built at Gateshead in 1889) for the Regional Open Air Museum, and this same organisation has also been able to preserve several clerestory coaches of about the same period which until 1966 were retained in use at Ashington by the National Coal Board. The earliest remaining coach, No 31 of the s & DR was built in 1846 by Messrs Horner & Wilkinson of Darlington and stood until recently on Stockton station; it has now been transferred to the National Transport Collection, York. An attempt is also being made, on behalf of the Regional Open Air Museum, to trace and preserve typical early goods vehicles and brake vans, before all are destroyed.

*Notes to this chapter are on p 199.*

# CHAPTER SEVEN

# *Power*

ALTHOUGH mention appears throughout this text of the various forms of power production used in the region, it will be useful to draw together details of some of the more significant examples.

## *Water power*

Water power, in its earliest form the most primitive form of power production, became an important factor in industrial development in the eighteenth and nineteenth centuries and consequently led to the evolution of fairly large and complex machinery. The watermills of the North East can be described as belonging to the 'upland' tradition as opposed to the 'lowland' tradition of counties further south and they are therefore important in the history of mill development. For the following note on the distinction, I am indebted to Kenneth Major:

> The differences between the upland tradition and the lowland tradition would seem at first sight to be rather arbitrary but in fact they are not. One cannot draw a hard line on the map and say that all mills to the west of the line are 'upland' in type and all to the east are 'lowland', but this is in fact nearly the case though there are many exceptions. With roughly 10,000 mills in the country the line is nearly correct statistically, and its best definition is the junction of limestone and chalk, ie Flamborough Head to Portland Bill.
>
> The pattern did not, in fact, become so split until the skilled millwork period of the 1830s, brought about by a change in farming patterns. The great arable corn farms of eastern England were just extending enclosure and their corn was produced for export to the great towns of the Midlands and London, while the 'upland' areas still consisted of mixed farms with a production of grain amounting to no more than local requirements. The differences between the two types, as evinced in the millwork are:
>
> *Lowland system.* Large mills with a great deal of storage. It was not

unknown for a mill in the south to carry 150 sacks in store at any one time. The mill was normally built on several storeys so that the grain could be processed and refined in a continuous flow down through the building after being ground. Hoists were therefore quite advanced in design and often operated through lucams on the face of the building as well as inside. The wheels were large, usually with the water entry at about 9 o'clock to 10 o'clock. Each wheel would normally drive four or more pairs of stones. The dressing of flour would normally involve about four stages.

*Upland system.* Small mills usually of only two or three storeys; no external hoists but internal hoists to the top floor from the ground. Small mills meant small storage space; hence the use of 'parcel' milling where the farmer only had four or five bags ground at a time. Milling was under multage and not by the buying and selling of grain and other products. The 'upland' wheels were usually overshot or high-breast shot: say 1 o'clock back to 10 o'clock for the water-entry positions. These wheels, though often large in diameter, would probably only have two pairs of stones attached.

What is important about many of the 'upland' mills is the further processes other than flour and grist production that were carried on:

1  Drying of wet grain in kilns over anthracite or coke hearths.
2  Production of roast oatmeal in kilns which consisted of hearth plates with knives turning the grain over ('crowdie' is a local term).
3  The production of pearl barley in special machines which consisted of stones rotating inside a perforated zinc cylinder, the perforations being nail holes knocked inwards so that the polishing of the barley grain was done on the sharp edges of the puncture.

Whilst the above are only generalisations, the distinction becomes clearer when one begins recording watermills. Basically it is the difference between a large trading mill and a small mill serving a community.

In the North East, mills are externally generally constructed in stone with a pantile or (in later examples) slate roof. They are invariably well-built, often in coursed ashlar and with well-formed window and door openings. Most of the mills had large overshot waterwheels; because of this there were often extensive leat systems and wooden troughs frequently carried water some distance from the streams. These high-level troughs sometimes enabled mills to be constructed in places which might otherwise not have been suitable.

For example the mill (now gutted) at Riding Mill stands by the road-side, and the wooden leat carried water over the gateway which gave access to a yard and land adjoining and behind the mill. This leat runs some distance along the top of the boundary wall alongside the road. Because of their size, the waterwheels were usually made of wood, with iron fittings, though there are a number of all-iron wheels, generally somewhat smaller and often associated with farms. The millwork is very much of the same pattern throughout the region.

Most of the remaining watermills have been corn mills, some on a commercial scale, others attached to farms, and ancillary machinery in several of these includes rotary drying kilns and pearl-barley machines. Nevertheless, water power in the region has been used in the past to drive such varied industrial plant as paper-works, flax mills, snuff mills, blanket mills, flint mills, oil-seed crushing plant and even a slate-pencil works.

An outstanding example of a corn mill is at Felton Park, Northum-berland, where three breast-wheels drove a total of six pairs of stones, a pearl-barley machine, flour screens, an oat-roaster and rotary oat-drying kiln, oatmeal-making plant, shakers and sieves. Other inter-esting corn mills are at Weldon Bridge and Ford, Northumberland; Wolviston and Coatham Mundeville, County Durham; and Brignall in Yorkshire.

*Wind power*

Wind power once held an important place in north-east industrial development, for although most remaining examples of the use of this form of power (and they mostly ruinous) have been for corn milling, wind power has also been used for threshing, snuff grinding (Chim-ney Mill, Newcastle), stone-grinding, oil-seed crushing and, par-ticularly during the eighteenth century, for colliery pumping.

Most of the remaining mills show well-built ashlar stone towers, several of quite considerable height, for example at Elwick, County Durham, and Woodhorn, Northumberland. Only one has any outward appearance of being complete: Fulwell Mill, Monkwearmouth, which was preserved by Sunderland Corporation in 1958. It is no longer workable as, for safety reasons, only a skeleton framework of the sails was kept.

## Horse power

Horse power[1] will be more fully mentioned in Chapter Nine for, though the horse has not provided a significant quantity of industrial power since the late-eighteenth century (when even engineers of Smeaton's stature were still using horses to drive factories), horse-wheels have been used on farms for threshing within living memory.

Two other horse-powered machines still existing in the region are both from County Durham and were both used in the coal industry. At Waterhouses Colliery (now closed) was a 'crab' used to raise pump spears; this is now dismantled and stored for the Regional Open Air Museum. At East Herrington still stands a water-pumping station, originally powered by steam and later by electricity, where the pump spears were also raised by horse power. This group, built as late as 1898 to 1900 is typically mid-nineteenth century in character and must have been one of the last horse-machines to work, for a horse was occasionally used as recently as the 1950s to raise the pump for repair. It is being retained for incorporation in the Regional Open Air Museum.

## Hydraulic power

Hydraulic power is important in the region on account of the activities of W. G. (later Lord) Armstrong, who in 1840 produced an efficient hydraulic engine, Fig 28. In 1847 he set up the Elswick Engine Works at Newcastle, which manufactured hydraulic machinery although it became better known in later years for its ordnance. A notable hydraulically-powered structure was Newcastle's Swing Bridge of 1876 (now driven electrically). The nearby (now demolished) Co-operative Society's grain warehouses on the Quay-side contained hydraulically-powered hoists, elevators and cranes, some of which have been collected by the Regional Open Air Museum.

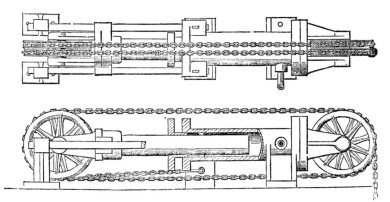

28   Typical hydraulically-powered machine. Part of a crane, as illustrated by W. G. Armstrong, in a description of his hydraulic machinery, written by him in 1854

One very good example of an hydraulic engine still remains, though now out of use, in the timber yard of the Allenheads estate. Thomas Sopwith, who was agent for the lead-mining works of that area, was a friend of Armstrong and a great believer in hydraulic power. He installed at least five hydraulic engines, mostly under-ground, and although one or more of these may still be in position, this Allenheads example can at least be easily examined.

A curious use of hydraulic power and one which demonstrates Armstrong's faith in his machinery, carried rather to an extreme, is at Crag End Farm, Rothbury, Northumberland. Here, on his estate, Lord Armstrong constructed a silo with hydraulic rams to compress the silage. At the same farm are water-turbines, also designed by Armstrong: one to drive a thresher, the other to drive a chaff cutter.[2]

## Steam power

Steam power, doubtless once the most important power-source in the region, is now represented by only a few scattered examples. These fall within the categories of colliery winding, coal haulage, water pumping (public utility) and agricultural threshing.

At the time of writing there are only two remaining vertical colliery winding engines both out of steam, at Elemore and Beamish (both in County Durham). There is only one coal haulage engine, of 1834, existing in the region. This was sited at Warden Law, south of Sunderland and is now dismantled and stored for the Regional Open Air Museum.

Public water-supply-pumping steam engines in County Durham, now all out of use, stand at Ryhope, Dalton (Cold Hesledon)[3] and Darlington. The first is a fine pair of beam engines of 1868, built by R. & W. Hawthorn of Newcastle; the second a pair of Cornish non-rotative engines of 1877; and the third a beam engine built by Teesdale Brothers in 1903, and still very occasionally steamed.

## Gas

Once of industrial importance in the region, gas making is now rapidly being phased out, as elsewhere, in favour of North Sea gas and gasworks are being demolished as they become redundant. Probably the best remaining gasworks buildings in the region are at North Shields and these now have only a short life. Town gas is still produced at the Consett works of the Steel Board, for use on the plant.

It may be of interest to mention the small hand-fired gasworks (from Milnthorpe near Kendal) which have now been dismantled and transported, with the aid of the Northern Gas Board, to Beamish, the site of the new Regional Open Air Museum. This small works which is to be re-erected in the urban area of the museum, is one of the last hand-fired gasworks in England; the only other known one being that of Fakenham in Norfolk, which is being preserved *in situ* by the Science Museum.

*Electricity*

Electricity is the final power-source to be mentioned here, and once more the region has a few 'firsts' to its credit. Although not the first area to generate a public supply, Newcastle was the first station to generate by turbine. The Newcastle & District Electric Light Co Ltd, was registered on 14 January 1889, and its Forth Banks power station went into commission in January 1890 with an initial equipment of two 75kW Parsons turbo-alternators constructed by Messrs Clarke, Chapman, Parsons & Co at Gateshead and supplied with steam from three Lancashire boilers. One of these steam turbines is now preserved in the entrance hall of Stella South power station. When in 1901, the Neptune Bank power station was opened, the Newcastle Electric supply was delivering electricity over what was probably the most widespread interconnected power system in the country.[4]

The first turbo-generator in the world was constructed by Sir Charles Parsons (who became managing director of Clarke, Chapman, Parsons & Co) in 1884. It was a DC unit developing about 75 amps at 100 volts when running at 18,000rpm. This historic machine is preserved in the Science Museum, London.

In 1878, Joseph Swan of Newcastle and Thomas Edison independently produced successful carbon-filament electric lamps and the question of priority was warmly debated. Litigation was wisely avoided by an agreement to amalgamate their interests and to this end the Edison & Swan United Electric Light Co was registered on 26 October 1883. The first public demonstration of electric lighting on a large scale by means of incandescent lamps had been given in Newcastle on 10 October 1880. Before that, in 1878, Sir William Armstrong had put a small hydro-electric plant on his estate, to generate current for the lighting of his picture gallery at Cragside.

In 1883 J. H. Holmes opened his electrical works in Portland Road, Newcastle, and in the following year he manufactured the first quick-break switch which, in modified form, found universal usage.

And, continuing the pioneering railway spirit of the region, the North East Railway Company was the first important British railway company to electrify a portion of its track: the suburban line between Newcastle and Benton, inaugurated in 1903.

*Notes to this chapter are on p 201.*

# CHAPTER EIGHT

# Manufacturing

SOME manufactures such as nails, bricks and pottery have already been dealt with in previous chapters. Here an attempt is made to give some account of several of the more major industries which have been important to the economy of the North East and to the lives of its people.

## SHIPBUILDING

When one considers manufacturing industries in the North East, one immediately thinks of shipbuilding and engineering, though the former at least has virtually destroyed its tangible history as it has developed. A shipyard is essentially a space on which a ship can be built and, after that ship has been launched, little of the actual process of building remains. The situation, from the industrial archaeologist's standpoint, has moreover not been helped by the many takeovers and yard closures of recent decades, for after each closure the movable equipment, machinery and tools are sold off and only the open yard is left. We must therefore leave this particular industry largely to the historian and in this connection David Dougan's recent *History of North East Shipbuilding* will be a useful guide. Surprisingly this story has never before been told in comprehensive form, despite the many major achievements.

We know that, at the very end of the seventeenth century, Ambrose Crowley sited his manufactory for nails, anchors, chains, etc in the North East almost entirely because of the growing shipbuilding industry.[1] Only thirty years or so later (1727) Daniel Defoe in his *Tour Through England and Wales* wrote: 'Newcastle is a spacious, extended, infinitely populous place. . . . They build ships here to perfection, I mean as to strength and firmness and to bear the sea, and as the coal trade occasions a demand for such strong ships, a great many are built here.'

The nineteenth century was, in shipbuilding as in so many north-eastern industries, a time of innovation. For example, a Newcastle colliery owner decided to build an iron collier and the *John Bowes* was launched in 1852, built by the General Iron Screw Collier Company which had been formed by Charles Palmer and his brother George. The first iron vessel had been built in this country as early as 1787, and the first iron ship built in the North East was the *Star* of South Shields (1839), but it was an ambitious, determined young man, Charles Palmer, who recognised that in iron vessels, propelled by steam, lay the future success of the north-eastern coal industry. The railway development of the 1840s had opened up a new source of coal for London—the Midlands and South Yorkshire coalfield—and the traditional coastal coal shipments were threatened.

Naturally not everyone was convinced, for the *John Bowes* cost £10,000 to build as against £1,000 for a sailing collier. On her very first journey to London, however, she proved her value, for she was loaded with 650 tons of coal in 4hr, took 48hr to reach the capital, 1 day to discharge and 2 days for the return journey. In 5 days she had done as much work as would have taken a sailing vessel 2 months to do.[2] There can be little doubt of the success of iron colliers, and John Bowes & Partners saw their business grow to an annual 1¼ million tons in the next twenty-five years. (John Bowes, the colliery owner, after whom this first screw-propelled iron collier was named, was an illegitimate son of the 10th Earl of Strathmore and well-known for his magnificent art collection housed in the Bowes Museum at Barnard Castle.)

An important innovation in the *John Bowes* was the introduction of water ballast, pumped out by the engines which powered the screw propeller. The extension of the ballast-hills along the banks of the Tyne was thus reduced even if the ensured increase of coal shipments was to lead to ever larger pit heaps. It is interesting to speculate upon another possible side-effect of the *John Bowes* for, prior to the introduction of water-ballast, loaded ballast had in part been used by Tyneside industries, notably those of the chemicals and glass. Did the reduction in ballast-loads conveniently coincide with the gradual decline of the chemical industry through other causes, or was there some closer effect?

As for the *John Bowes* herself, she had an eventful career, changing owners, flag and name several times. Variously named *Spec*, *Transit* and *Carolina*, and being at times used as a general-cargo ship and as a cable-layer, she eventually sank in a storm off Bilbao in 1933, the same year as Palmer's shipyard collapsed.

If the Tyne was early in the field with iron-built ships, the Wear and Tees were not far behind. In 1852 the first iron ship built at Sunderland, the 77 ton *Loftus*, was launched; Stockton's first iron ship, the *Advance*, followed in 1854, and Middlesbrough's first iron ship, the *De Brus*, was launched in 1858.

Yet though all these and other yards in the North East were establishing their reputations, no firm could match the meteoric rise of Palmer's. Palmer himself attributed his success to his experiment with the *John Bowes*, the current development of iron shipbuilding and the continued large supply of coals to the London market. He estimated that the total tonnage of iron ships launched on the Tyne, Wear and Tees in 1862 was over 57,000 tons. About 38,000 tons of iron were used that year. His own firm obtained most of its ironstone from its own mines in the Cleveland Hills, shipped from Port Mulgrave. He had four blast furnaces at Jarrow, together with rolling mills, and his company was able to complete the full process 'from ore to finished ship'. Success led to success and during the late eighties and early nineties, British shipbuilding produced four out of every five ships launched in the whole world and the North East alone produced on occasions more than 40 per cent of the world total.

From this period another 'first' can be credited to the North East, and one for which we can still see tangible remains—the advent of turbine propulsion in the shape of *Turbinia*. This innovation was the

work of Charles Parsons, youngest son of the 3rd Earl of Rosse, who
held a four year's engineering apprenticeship at the Elswick works of
Sir William Armstrong before acquiring a junior partnership in the
Gateshead firm of Clarke, Chapman & Company, where he was put
in charge of their newly-formed electrical department. His first work
on turbines was therefore connected with the generation of electricity
(p 156), though it seems that from the start he had appreciated the
part that turbines could play in marine propulsion. His chance came
in 1894 when, after a quarrel with Clarke, Chapman, he severed his
connection and set up his own firm, the Marine Steam Turbine Co,
at Heaton. Here he immediately began to build and equip the
*Turbinia* but, although the Admiralty was kept fully informed of
his difficulties and successes, their lordships showed little real
interest despite the revolutionary speeds being achieved in tests after
1896. Parsons therefore decided on a public demonstration and, at
the naval review at Spithead in June 1897, the solid pomp and splen-
dour was shaken by his tiny ship whipping up and down the lines at
an unprecedented speed of more than 30 knots. The Admiralty was
convinced and turbine propulsion was soon fully accepted. *Turbinia*
continued to advertise this new principle and in 1900 she appeared
at the great Paris exhibition, demonstrating her speed along the river
Seine. A few years later she was lifted on to a cradle on the quay of
the Marine Steam Turbine Company where she attracted interest
until 1926 when she was offered to the London Science Museum.
Space there being limited, the after 45ft of hull, complete with turbines and propeller shafts, was cut off and taken to London, and in
1944 a 15ft section of the bow with wheelhouse and boiler was pre-
sented to Newcastle Corporation. In 1959 the Science Museum felt
unable, due to reorganisation, to retain the after section on display
and arrangements were made to bring the two parts together once
more. A new centre-section replica was constructed and a special
building to house the restored *Turbinia* was opened to the public at
the Newcastle Museum of Science & Industry in September 1961.[3]

On a more sombre note, one should record another and earlier

K

'first' for the region—a lifeboat. In 1789 the *Adventure* of Newcastle sank off South Shields, only 300yd from the shore, and her crew dropped, one by one, into the raging breakers in the presence of thousands of spectators, none of whom dared to put off to the rescue. An excited meeting among the people of South Shields followed; a committee was formed, and a prize was offered for the best model of a lifeboat. Of the many plans put forward, those of William Wouldhave, a painter, and Henry Greathead, a boatbuilder, were selected. The committee awarded the prize to the latter and, combining the good points of both designs, gave an order to Greathead for the construction of the boat. This first put to sea on 30 January 1790. It did good service and Greathead received £1,200 from Parliament. The names of Henry Greathead and William Wouldhave were inscribed on a memorial erected at South Shields on the occasion of the 1890 centenary. This takes the form of a clocktower and stands at the end of Ocean Road, leading towards the pier, whilst beneath a nearby canopy is preserved an early example of a lifeboat.[4]

### MECHANICAL ENGINEERING

One may presume that engineering skills have been practised in the North East for as long as coal mining has been a significant industrial feature. Thus when the first attempt at mechanisation of any aspect of mining was being introduced during the early years of the eighteenth century, it appears that there were sufficient engineers of the appropriate calibre ready at hand: men like Henry Beighton, who in 1718 made a notable contribution to Newcomen's outstanding invention of a practical steam engine.[5] Beighton's modification to the valve operation proved to be such a simplification that it remained largely unaltered during the lifetime of the Newcomen engine. Since the first of these to be erected in the North East was probably that at Tanfield Lea in 1714, Beighton was clearly not drawing on vast experience of Newcomen engines but rather on his experience as a general engineer.

One can also assume that the readiness with which the Newcomen engine was adopted in the North East also indicates a general familiarity with relatively advanced engineering. By 1733 these engines were quite widespread there and indeed the local founders were leading the way in the production of larger and cheaper cast-brass cylinders than the 28in ones available elsewhere.

By 1752 the north-east foundries were, it seems, resting on their laurels, for it is known that William Brown, a prolific engineer from Throckley, obtained a 47in diameter cast-iron cylinder from Coalbrookdale in Shropshire for the new engine which he was building at Throckley Colliery. Brown was undoubtedly the leading engineer in the north at this time, being credited with the construction of twenty-two such engines in the Northumberland and Durham coalfield between 1756 and 1776, including a 74in engine for Walker Colliery, fed by four boilers and the largest ever built up to that date. Alas, it would appear that nothing remains of Brown's works.

In 1765, Joseph Oxley, a contemporary of Brown's, made the first notable attempt to use steam for the direct winding of coal at Hartley Colliery,[6] an achievement which brought James Watt amongst others as an interested observer.[7] Although satisfactory for a while, ultimate success was only accomplished by Watt's later steam engine with rotary action.

By this time the large engineering and foundry establishment of Hawks, Crawshey & Co of Gateshead had come into being, but it was not until the last years of the eighteenth and the early years of the nineteenth century that the big names of recent times became established. Amongst these were Murray & Co (Chester-le-Street, 1793); Losh, Wilson & Bell (Walker, 1807); R. & W. Hawthorn (Newcastle, 1817); R. Stephenson & Co (Newcastle, 1823); Gilkes, Wilson & Co (Middlesbrough, 1844); W. G. Armstrong & Co (Elswick, 1847); Morrison & Co (Newcastle, 1853); Thompson & Co (Newcastle, 1856); Joy & Co (Middlesbrough, 1862). The industrial revolution was now in full swing, the engineers of the North East playing leading roles. The above-named firms were involved in a host of products including mill work, colliery engineering, winding engines, pumping engines, farm engines, agricultural machines, blowing engines, locomotives, steam hammers, hydraulic engines and a variety of smaller engineering products.

In the field of locomotive engineering the North East gave birth to Hedley, Blenkinsop, Stephenson and Hawthorn, all of whom served apprenticeships at north-eastern collieries as firemen and colliery engineers. Fortunately such men became legends in their own time so that various tangible remains of their labours still exist for our inspection. The pre-eminent locomotive building firms of Robert Stephenson & Co and R. & W. Hawthorn, Leslie & Co carried on the early traditions of these men and some of their locomotives remain.

There were other firms in the North East who built locomotives, Gilkes, Wilson & Co and Sir W. G. Armstrong & Co, being amongst them. Of the latter, more must be said for, although in 1847 Armstrong built a unique condensing locomotive engine *The Flying Dutchman*, this proved a complete failure, the advantages of sub-atmospheric condenser pressures being easily outweighed by the higher boiler pressures of his rivals' engines. Armstrong again dabbled in locomotive building in the 1860s, but never found it financially rewarding.

But such failures were not the mark of Armstrong, the son of a Cumberland man who became a respected corn merchant in Newcastle having his works at Cowgate. Armstrong, unlike his rather conservative father, had an unusual inventive flair and in 1847 set up his modest factory in the green fields of Elswick where the firm of Vickers Armstrong stands today. He intended to commercialise and market some of the ideas which he had formulated in earlier years and indeed successfully introduced his concept of developing power from water by incorporating hydraulic machines to such items as cranes, forging presses, mining machinery, dock gates, the Tower Bridge at London and the Newcastle Swing Bridge. The other pillar of Armstrong's success became ordnance and, although his first invention—

the rifled cannon—was not an immediate success in 1855, it had been so modified by 1858 that it was then accepted as unrivalled. From then on his growth in ordnance interests kept pace with the growth in general engineering and further diversification brought ship-building to Elswick. The Museum of Science & Engineering in New-castle holds various items relating to Armstrong's early days includ-ing a hydro-electric machine (1840) for the generation of electricity from high-pressure steam, and the Swing Bridge still functions and incorporates part of Armstrong's original equipment.

By the approach and start of the twentieth century, general en-gineering was no longer a virile and growing force in the North East, only locomotive building and armaments remained strong. Failure to diversify from these led to a gradual contraction in general engineer-ing which probably continues today.

If the heyday of general engineering in the North East is past, we are therefore all the more fortunate to have some reminder of earlier achievements. We will probably always notice the effect which the railway and locomotive builders have had on our pattern of living and, in a more tangible form, several of the locomotives have been preserved. In addition, such magnificent works of engineering as the Ryhope pumping engines (R. & W. Hawthorn, 1868), perfect in their symmetry, will we hope be preserved. More modest but no less significant is the farm engine by Gilkes Wilson & Co (1852), held for use in the new Regional Open Air Museum. Many items relating to general engineering in the North East are held by the Newcastle Museum of Science & Engineering and undoubtedly others remain still hidden.

Thus there may yet be work for the industrial archaeologist in this field, and for the industrial historian there would appear to be some very pertinent questions. He might, for example, ponder on the decline of general engineering in the North East, seek out reasons for the absence of any significant machine-tool industry, or examine the failure of projects such as the motor car manufactured by Sir W. G. Armstrong & Co. It may well be that in future years there will be very little industrial archaeology of general engineering in the North East, for evidence of such skills may disappear altogether.

## CHEMICALS

The North East is today, around Billingham and Wilton, the home of a large and thriving modern chemical industry, whose development has little connection with our historical story. On the other hand the region has also seen the development and decline of two independent and important chemical industries: one on Tyneside, the other in Cleveland. The Tyneside alkali trade was a logical growth based more on available facilities than on local sources of material, whereas the Cleveland alum industry, though smaller, was the result of indigenous raw materials. Both have effectively disappeared, leaving only traces for the industrial archaeologist.

### Tyneside alkali trade

The Tyneside alkali trade may be said to have its origins in the growing textile industry of the late eighteenth and early nineteenth centuries. The increased emphasis on manufacturing processes in the second half of the eighteenth century, which we know as the Industrial Revolution, was particularly concerned with the mechanisation of the textile industry, and the resultant increased output of cloth called for an increased amount of soap, bleach and dyes. Glass too began to be demanded in larger quantities as industrial requirements and standards of living rose. These problems of production and the development of entirely new industries resulted in a chemical revolution, and much of the pioneer work which led to the establishment of the chemical industry took place on Tyneside. Many of the discoveries and inventions made here had profound effects on the prosperity of the nation. The alkali trade was of great importance as can be seen from the equations:

$$\text{Alkali} + \text{Fat} \longrightarrow \text{Soap}$$
$$\text{Alkali} + \text{Sand} + \text{Lime} \longrightarrow \text{Glass}$$

Paradoxically, it was the bad state of navigability of the Tyne (the river to which we have attributed the growth of the coal industry) which encouraged the growth of new industries. The fact was that the river, ideal for the early shipment of coals, became less suitable as years passed. Larger ships experienced difficulty in passing upstream and uncontrolled tipping of ballast waste and coal spillage added to the difficulties. Consequently, only the best coal could fetch a price that made shipment worthwhile, handled twice as it was, from staithe to keel and keel to collier. Other, smaller and poorer coal could not be exported and much was stored underground or burnt at the pit head. Salt-boiling to produce salt and the coking of coal, as we have seen, absorbed much of this cheap coal, but a new industry sprang up on Tyneside in the seventeenth century also encouraged by this cheap fuel—glassmaking (p 173). Until the beginning of that century glasshouses were to be found where wood abounded, but the growing scarcity of timber for shipbuilding led to an edict of 1615 forbidding the use of timber for glassmaking, and the glassmakers were obliged to move to other areas in search of replacement fuel.

Yet glassmakers required not only fuel but sand and alkali. The former could be brought as ballast by returning colliers and no doubt was an added reason for the selection of this particular coalfield. Alkali, in an early process, required coal both as fuel and raw material and hence the development of this manufacturing industry. The order of events on Tyneside may thus be seen: glass followed the coal and chemicals followed the glass.

The term alkali, limited in this context to the common chemicals soda and potash (more scientifically termed sodium carbonate and potassium carbonate), comes from an Arabic word meaning calcined ashes; and this gives a clue to early processes for its preparation. Wood was burned and the residue extracted with water which was afterwards evaporated in large iron pots over a fire. The ash left in the pots, the pot-ash, was sold to glassmakers and salt-boilers. When seaweed was used in place of wood the ash contained additionally a proportion of soda. Kelp or calcined seaweed was produced at North Shields and Whitley Bay and in 1674 Sir Ralph Delaval was receiving rent from kelp burners at Hartley. Local sources were, however, insufficient for the rising demand and a great deal of kelp and potash was being imported by 1800.

Another process for making soda, of greater historical significance to the region, started with brine from which salt was recovered by simple evaporation. In 1798 John Losh and the Earl of Dundonald took a lease on a rich supply of brine being pumped from Walker Pit near Newcastle. The heavy salt tax of the day would have incurred a duty of £36 per ton on the evaporated salt, had not the Government permitted the process to be duty free, subject to the salt being spoiled for domestic use by an admixture of soot and ashes. For twenty-five years, until the reduction of the tax in 1823 and its repeal in 1825 when imported salt from Cheshire became economically possible, the process flourished (p 114) and undoubtedly allowed Tyneside to develop leadership in alkali production.[8] Sulphuric acid was required for subsequent treatment of the brine and was made from copperas (iron sulphate) by roasting this in an oven. The copperas was made by exposing iron pyrites (or 'coal brasses' or 'fool's gold') to weathering for several years. This small industry itself was widespread wherever pyrites were found among the coal, and there are records showing that copperas was being made at Seaton Sluice. In 1812, however, a lead-lined chamber was erected at Bill Quay for the better production of sulphuric acid, and in 1821 another was constructed at Walker. Bleaching powder, another chemical required for the textile industry, began to be manufactured at Walker in 1830, and from waste products yet another substance, hypo, began to be converted in 1852 for use in the paper industry.

Alkali works sprang up along the banks of the Tyne as the nineteenth century advanced. They were especially to be found clustering at points where transport facilities were particularly good, such as at Walker, Wallsend and Jarrow. But the most remarkable group was that which grew up between South Shore at Gateshead and Bill Quay, including Friar's Goose, Felling and Heworth Shores. Little remains of these buildings though the industry of this area is fortunately fairly well documented.

There were also works engaged in the production of colours— lamp-black, turpentine and copperas—whilst within the works were also to be found cooperages, where barrels for soda and bleaching powder were made, saw-pits, smithies and plumbers' shops.

Despite all this mid-century prosperity, by the end of the nineteenth century the heavy chemical industry was on the way to complete disappearance from the banks of the Tyne. A new process had been developed which did not require cheap coal and was therefore sited more economically over salt deposits. Thus the northern centre of the trade moved from Tyneside to Teesside. As early as 1882 three Tyneside firms, Allhusons', Tennant's and Jarrow Chemical Company had begun to establish salt works around Haverton Hill near Billingham, attracted by large underground salt deposits. For the purposes of the older Leblanc process the brine (as it was extracted) had to be evaporated to dryness, but for the newer Solvay process evaporation was not necessary. Thus, as Campbell has written in his *The Old Tyneside Chemical Trade* (1964): 'the three great Tyneside firms who began working salt on Teesside prepared the way for their own destruction'.

The visible remains of the old Tyneside chemical industry are disappointingly few, the most notable monuments being the waste heaps at Felling and Heworth, both very carefully constructed. Some of the ground works of Allhusen's can still be traced at Gateshead's South Shore, adjacent to Clarke Chapmans. For the rest, the chemical sites were generally built-over by the shipyards. W. A. Campbell of the School of Chemistry, Newcastle University, writes that:

The most promising new field is likely to be the observation of coloured strata where public works digging is taking place: black manganese dioxide and blue and red iron colours are most likely. Prussian blue was found when Reyrolle's built their new office block at Hebburn, and current landscaping of the river front at Friars Goose has revealed black calcium sulphide waste (thixotropic like quicksand), fine red iron oxide from the copper extraction process and yellow arsenic sulphide from the manufacture of arsenic-free sulphuric acid. There are still street and public house names extant, though even these are mostly in demolition areas. All industrial archaeologists should visit (for sentimental reasons) the Alkali Hotel at Jarrow.

## Soap making

A natural corollary of the Tyneside alkali trade was, as we have seen, the growth of soap making, and the cheap Leblanc process for making alkali from common salt (introduced to this country about 1814) plus the introduction about the same date of vegetable oils in place of olive oil or tallow, made cheap soap possible. As new sea routes opened up, new raw materials became available—palm, cotton seed and coconut oils. But, although the Duke of Wellington by his personal example popularised daily baths among the upper and middle classes, among the working population the consumption of soap was still low because of its cost and the lack of domestic water supplies. It was the cholera epidemic of 1848 which forced Gladstone to repeal the tax on soap, which at its highest had equalled the cost of manufacture. After more than 200 years padlocks were taken off the soap-kettle lids, for these had been locked every night by the excise officer to prevent the illegal production of tax-free soap overnight. Fig 29, a contemporary illustration of soap boiling, shows a locked soap-kettle lid of the late 1840s.

Thomas Hedley, born the son of a Northumberland farmer in 1809, began employment with a firm of grocers, tallow chandlers and wine merchants at Gateshead. In about 1840 he entered into partnership with the firm in the establishment of a soap manufactory at Newcastle. He eventually acquired the business and carried it on under the designation of Thomas Hedley & Co. This business grew and prospered and in the early years of this century began acquiring other soap manufacturing concerns; in 1926 Fairy soap was introduced as a national brand. In 1930 the company was in turn acquired by the Procter & Gamble Company of Cincinnati, and continues to be a major industrial concern on Tyneside. Like so many prosperous works, it has largely destroyed its early buildings as it has developed.

29   Soap boiling. A contemporary illustration of about 1849, showing part of a soap works

### The Cleveland alum industry

If little visible remains of the great Tyneside chemical industries, a certain amount can be discerned of the smaller alum industry of north-east Yorkshire. Although today alum is a commodity of relatively small importance, it was in the past of very real value, being used in tanning and as a mordant in dyeing, and also medicinally. Indeed the manufacture of alum has been called the earliest chemical industry.

In Elizabethan times, alum works near Guisborough were extracting the chemical from local deposits of aluminous shale. These Newbank works are recorded as having been opened in about 1595 and closed in 1650, though they were again worked for a time, possibly in the early-eighteenth century. The quarry is visible, and nearby is a big hill of bright-red calcined shale. Early in the seventeenth century the alum industry came under the Crown and after various difficulties workmen were brought in from the Low Countries, so that by the 1630s the alum mines were being successfully worked. The Crown's interest was given up in 1679. Subsequently the growth of the textile industry, the concomitant of the Industrial Revolution, caused an ever-growing demand for alum. By 1769, for example, sixteen alum works in Yorkshire were producing 5,000 tons annually. This was probably the highest annual production, for by 1815 the figure was down to 3,000 tons and in 1846 to 1,100 tons. The Yorkshire industry finally closed about 1870.

The process of extracting alum began first with the quarrying of an aluminous shale which was broken into small pieces and stacked into a clamp or large pile composed of alternate layers of alum shale and brushwood. The heap was set on fire when about 4ft high, then the piling up and calcining went on simultaneously and in the case of large clamps lasted several weeks. Next the calcined shale was barrowed to steeping pits filled with water where the required chemical was dissolved. This liquor was then boiled in the alum house and, after subsequent treatment, crystals of alum were collected, washed and re-crystallised and finally packed for transport in casks or sacks.

Apart from the early Guisborough site already mentioned, better remains can be seen at Kettleness, where the foundations of the alum house are visible and especially at Boulby where there are an alum house, quarries, steeping pits and even an uncompleted calcining clamp.

## *Matches*

Finally, whilst nothing remains on the ground, and the industry was not started in the region, it is probably relevant to mention here the name of John Walker of Stockton-onTees, a pharmacist who, in 1827, invented the first friction match. His account book recording his first sales of this product and specimens of his matches are preserved in the Bryant & May collections and at least some of the contents of his shop are preserved for eventual use in the Regional Open Air Museum.

### GLASSMAKING[9]

The earliest information we have of industrial activity in the region comes from Bede, who recorded that the art of glassmaking was taught to the English by foreigners brought from Gaul to glaze the windows of the abbey built at Wearmouth in AD 675. Yet the skills apparently died and a thousand years elapsed before the industry reappeared.

This time it was cheap coal, which perforce became acceptable as fuel, that attracted the industry to Tyneside in the early-seventeenth century. According to his own evidence, Sir Robert Mansel, who in 1615 obtained a patent for making glass with coal, after trying to start works in London, the Isle of Purbeck and Milford Haven, 'was enforced for his last refuge contrary to all men's opinion to make triall at Newcastle upon Tyne where after the expence of many thousand pounds that worke for window-glasse was effected with Newcastle Cole'.

Many glassmakers from Lorraine found their way to the Newcastle area in the early years of the seventeenth century and, although we do not know for certain exactly when, probably less than a century elapsed before they crossed the Tyne to set up works at South

Shields. Here an early specialisation in plate glass proved successful, and by 1827 there were eight large works. Through the years up to 1845 the excise returns show that more plate glass was made at South Shields than at any other town in the country. Plate glass was made by running molten glass on a metal table and rolling it to an even thickness, whereas crown glass which preceded it was made by blowing out a globe and cutting it to produce a roughly circular sheet with a large knob or bullion in the centre. This sheet was then cut up into economical pieces, resulting in the small window panes so familiar in medieval and seventeenth-century windows. The centre piece, spoiled by the bullion, was of less value and often used in cottage and early factory windows. Known as 'bull's eye' glass it has today changed its value and amusingly enough is now much sought-after.

Crown glass had been a big manufacture along the Tyne, but by 1850 all the works there making it had closed. The sheet glass which replaced it was extensively manufactured at Sunderland, especially after the foundation of the Wear Glassworks by James Hartley in 1842. Hartley invented a process for making a new kind of sheet glass called rolled-plate, rather like unpolished plate glass. This achieved a world-wide reputation and was used for the Crystal Palace in 1851. At one time a flourishing firm, Hartley's occupied a large site on Hylton Road, Sunderland, but the works was closed and dismantled in 1896.

Blown bottles, another important product of the industry, were replaced in the mid-nineteenth century by the cheaper pressed-glass bottles. These were blown within metal moulds, thereby increasing speed of production and accuracy of size and shape. By 1850 there were at least forty bottle works in the North East and their products still turn up occasionally and can be seen in local museums.

One should also mention the Hartley glasshouses which used Seaton Sluice as their port and which, like the other north-eastern glassworks, were based on the advantages of local coal, and ashes and pot-clay brought in as ballast. This works was founded by Thomas

Delaval in 1763 to produce bottles, which it did in prodigious quantities, only to close in 1870 (Fig 23).

Thus, during the eighteenth and nineteenth centuries glassmaking became one of the major manufacturing industries of the North East, whilst today it is only of residual importance. Apart from the large works of James Jobling at Sunderland where Pyrex brand ovenware is produced, and the Lemington, Northumberland, works of GEC Ltd, nothing remains of an industry which as late as 1911 employed almost 3,000 men. The chief building of this industry still standing is the fine glasshouse at Lemington, possibly the largest of the only five remaining in the country.

## LEAD PRODUCTS

The industrial value of lead has largely lain in its malleability, its low melting point and, in the form of lead carbonate, in its use as a paint pigment. Rolled out to a sheet it was widely used as a roofing material, being easily applied to a shaped surface, yet waterproof. Drawn out as a pipe it was used for water supply and, being easily cast, it was used for water tanks, ornate pump-heads and the like. Examples of all these uses are widespread and need hardly be enumerated, but the works which produced so many of these materials in the region are now closed or thoroughly modernised.

### *Lead shot*

Few, if any, early buildings associated with lead products remain to attract our attention in the region. Until recently a fine lead-shot tower stood on the north bank of the Tyne at Elswick. Built in 1797 by Walkers, Fishwick & Co, it was one of four remaining in the country; the others being at Bristol (1783), Chester (1799) and Edmonton in Middlesex (1908). All these towers, and others now destroyed, followed a patent taken out in 1782 by William Watts, a Bristol plumber. The Bristol example was constructed by Watts who modified his house, adding a small tower, removing the floors of three rooms and sinking a shaft into the ground, by which means he obtained the equivalent of a tower about 130ft high. This historic building was demolished in 1968 and the Elswick shot tower was thus, for a short period, the oldest remaining example and certainly the most elegant.

When first built, the Elswick tower is said to have been 2ft out of the perpendicular and this was rectified by the hazardous expedient of digging down to the foundations and removing a certain amount of soil, when the tower righted itself. About 190ft high and 18ft in diameter at the base, it was built of brick, crowned with a stone cupola and lighted by a number of windows with fan-light tops. Inside, round the walls, was a fine stone spiral staircase with an iron balustrade.[10]

Molten lead was poured through a 'colander' or frame full of holes, into a vat of water at the foot of the tower, though part of the secret of good shot-forming lay in the addition of arsenic to the lead for hardening. The work was carried on by two men, known as runners: one at the top and one, the senior man, at the bottom. The shot-running floor at the top of the tower was provided with a furnace and melting pot and supplies of fuel and lead were sent up by a bucket hoist. About 5 tons of shot could be run per day and the top runner naturally tended to stay at the top for the whole of his shift. Messages concerned with the size of shot were therefore passed up by means of a small bucket on a rope, and such is conservatism that the suggestion of telephone communication was refused and this method of communication persisted until production was discontinued in 1951.[11]

Although only two towers now remain, others were in use last century together with converted mine shafts. At Alston in Cumberland, for example, there was a combined tower and shaft with a drift to the bottom of the shaft, and at Cockfield Fell in County Durham a coal shaft was used for shot making.[12]

## White lead

Passing now to another lead product, white lead or lead carbonate, at Willington Quay there is a threatened group of buildings, said to be the only ones so constructed in this country, for making it by the German 'chamber' process. The buildings were put up in 1898 and ceased work about 1950.[13]

White lead had earlier been made by the Dutch process, introduced to this country about 1780, and by 1850 Newcastle upon Tyne was described as a place where white lead was extensively manufactured by this method. A few remains of buildings used for this Dutch or 'stack' process exist, though completely altered. Small earthenware pots were filled with strong acetic acid, set side-by-side on a brick floor, embedded in a mixture of new and spent tan and covered by small pieces of thin cast lead. Wooden planks were then put across the whole and a second range of pots placed on them. In this way a stack of 8 or 10 layers of pots was built up in a brick chamber, to a height of some 25ft. At the Newcastle works it is recorded that a number of these stacks were in use, each stack containing about 12,000 pots and from 50 to 60 tons of lead. Soon after completion of a stack the tan began to ferment and the heat rose, causing the acetic acid to vaporise. This vapour, together with carbon dioxide from the fermentation, resulted in the formation of lead carbonate until, after about six weeks, fermentation ceased and the stack was dismantled.

The later German 'chamber' process required a range of brick-built compartments (Fig 30) with frequent light brick arches. Across these planks were set, and 'buckles' or strips of cast lead were then hung over the wood, starting at the top (by ladder). The chambers were heated by flues, and fumes of acetic acid and carbon dioxide entered through holes in the floor. After several weeks the chambers were cooled and emptied. Four men would contract to empty a chamber in four days. White lead is now made much more rapidly by a continuous process.

L

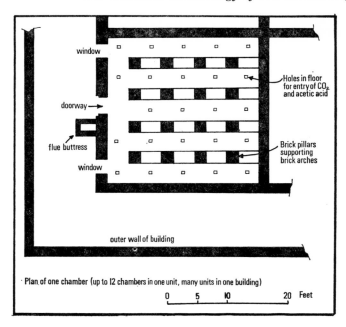

window

doorway →

flue buttress

window

Holes in floor
for entry of $CO_2$
and acetic acid

Brick pillars
supporting
brick arches

outer wall of building

Plan of one chamber (up to 12 chambers in one unit, many units in one building)

0    5    10         20   Feet

30    Lead works at Willington Quay. Lead strips were exposed
to vapour of acetic acid and carbon dioxide, thus being converted to white lead

TEXTILES, LEATHER AND ROPE

Apart from a flourishing leather trade at Hexham, which has left few
material remains, the textile and leather industries belong largely to
the southern part of our region and date from the end of the seventeenth century. Before that time spinning and weaving were widely
distributed domestic crafts, but not flourishing in any one place in
the region.

When Ralph Thoresby passed through Barnard Castle in 1694 he
mentioned leather as its chief industry and the town as 'now chiefly
famous for bridles', but another visitor forty years later remarked

that 'a great woollen manufactory of stockings' was carried on there. Carpets were a well-known Barnard Castle product and continued to be so long after the other worsted industries had gone. The water of the Tees was supposed to be well-suited to the production of bright colours and by 1827 there were five carpet factories in the town; the last closed in 1888. Across the river, just over the bridge in Startforth, still stands a five-storey mill built in 1760 to spin flax. Until thirty years ago it continued in use, making shoe-thread and having an extensive export trade. All the flax was imported.

Castle Eden was the scene of an important manufactory set up by a Mr Burdon in 1792 to make corduroys and sail cloth, but little if any trace can now be found.

Darlington has long been associated with spinning and weaving and was noted for its linen manufacture long before it gained its reputation for worsteds. *The Universal Magazine* of 1749 stated: 'It is the most noted place in the whole world for huckabacks, being made from half an ell to 3 yards wide. The price varies from 7d to 18s, the broad sort being made nowhere else.' Not all the linen thread was woven in Darlington: surrounding villages carried out weaving too. At Hurworth many houses had, until recently, sheds built in their back gardens where weaving was carried on and a thorough survey may still discover some of these. John Kendrew, a Darlington man, was the first to apply machinery to the spinning of flax. He had a flax mill on the Skerne as early as 1788, together with a spectacle mill, for he had also invented a method 'of grinding optical glasses of a true spherical form'. Later he moved to Haughton-le-Skerne, where his mill stood until recently, bearing the date 1782.

Around the middle of the eighteenth century it seems that the Peases began spinning and weaving worsted goods and, at the beginning of the nineteenth century, trade was so good that one large worsted manufactory in the town included about 300 looms and employed 100 combers and 5,000 hand spinners. So great was the demand, that the number of work-people in Darlington was insufficient and wool was sent to Scotland to be spun. After considerable

180    *The Industrial Archaeology of North-East England*

reduction in the textile trade early this century, Darlington is once more the home of a woollen industry—the modern works of Paton & Baldwin.

The shipping industry so prosperous on the north-east coast during the eighteenth and nineteenth centuries demanded large quantities of sail cloth and rope. In Sunderland alone in 1827 were 19 ropemakers and 20 sailmakers, but the substitution of wire for hemp and the disappearance of sail resulted in great reductions.[14] The first ever use of machinery for the continuous manufacture of rope was made at Webster's ropery at Deptford, Sunderland. This process was patented in 1797. Until that date all rope had to be made by a tedious and lengthy process on a rope walk somewhat longer than the required piece of rope. Longer pieces could only be made by splicing, a not-altogether satisfactory method for some purposes. Despite this invention, however, rope continued to be made at rope walks until well into the present century. Walks can be easily identified on old maps by their considerable length when compared with their small width, and all the ports and riverside towns of the North East had their walks, some now remembered only by nearby street-names.

PAPER MAKING

By 1700, paper mills had been established at Croxdale and Chopwell in County Durham and, throughout the next hundred years, the industry flourished in two general areas. One of these spread along the Derwent Valley, the Tyne tributaries and Upper Tynedale; the other was along the tributaries of the Wear near Durham.

In the first few years of the nineteenth century, at least eighteen mills were at work in County Durham alone: at Ewhurst, Lintzford, Shotley Grove, Blackhall, Chopwell, Lamesley, Urpeth and White-hill in the north; at Moorsley Banks, Relley, Stonebridge, Langley, Cornforth, Thinford, Hett, Butterly and Croxdale around Durham; and at Tudhoe in the south. The majority of these manufactured brown paper, although good quality paper was made at Lintzford,

Shotley Grove, Urpeth, Lamesley and Croxdale from quite an early date. Several of the mills were converted from fulling mills around 1800.

By the end of the nineteenth century most of the mills had ceased work, Lintzford being the last Durham mill to close: it was converted to a printing-ink factory in 1923. Very few traces of the industry now remain; the sole remaining factory (founded in 1763) being at Fourstones on the Tyne, 4 miles north-west of Hexham.

### FOODSTUFFS

There is little remarkable to note about the varied industries of food preparation in the region. Every town has had its brewery, often dating back at least 150 years, and water-powered corn milling has been carried on where the local markets required it and water power was adequate. Sweet forming, a trade which came into prominence in the last century, has continued locally into the middle of this; though national sweet makers are gradually putting local manufacturers out of business. The soft drinks industry was also widespread, in the early years of this century, subsequently becoming concentrated at a few large works. Neither of these two last-mentioned industries has left much for the industrial archaeologist in the way of buildings, though some equipment has been saved by the Regional Open Air Museum.

An interesting localised occupation has been that of salmon-fishing along the Tweed. Small boats of characteristic, almost-triangular plan and high prow still take the nets across the river and, though no longer required, ice-houses, where ice was stored in winter to serve for fish preservation throughout the season, can still be seen in Berwick-on-Tweed. This is also an appropriate point to mention domestic ice-houses, which could possibly be accepted as coming within the industrial archaeologist's interest. Little has been done to record these, though many doubtless await discovery and detailed examination.

Another fish industry is that of kippering, still carried on in a range of pantiled buildings at Craster. Long wooden vents along the ridge are similar to those sometimes seen on malthouses.

The many warehouses for foodstuffs, to be traced in the older ports, have already been mentioned (p 122). Such towns as Berwick, Alnmouth, Stockton and Yarm are particularly good places to find older examples of granaries and other food stores.

*Notes to this chapter are on p 201.*

CHAPTER NINE

# *Agriculture*

THIS is one of those occupations about which industrial archaeologists have been known to disagree. Should it, or should it not come within the scope of our studies? It is probably thoughts of the rustic scene and the bucolic countryman which cause some to eschew farming as an industry. Yet the buildings of the farm have been—and indeed are—specifically designed to suit their functions, and are eminently suitable for study, though often the older ones are nowadays used for a different purpose to that for which they were built. In a county now so heavily industrialised as Durham it is notable that, as late as 1832, about one-third of the 'labouring classes' were engaged in agriculture.[1] Such a large employer of labour can hardly be overlooked.

FARM LAYOUT

Just as changing demands and technology have caused industrial fluctuation and varied siting, so have agricultural functions and buildings been altered over the past three centuries. At times the price of corn led to this being the primary crop, when the soil and altitude would permit it; at others sheep or milk production or stock-rearing predominated. Each of these operations requires its own specialised buildings or equipment and hence the farm layout frequently demonstrates this historical development. Eastern Northumberland was, in the middle of the last century, a notable corn-growing region, yet the *Land Utilisation Survey* of 1945 (Fig 31) indicates this area as predominantly grazing and dairying. Such changes make it sometimes difficult to determine the original function of a building which may now be serving quite another purpose.

In addition to changes in land use, one finds that technological

183

changes such as replacing the horse by the tractor, have led to different building requirements; stabling for perhaps six or ten horses, 'tack' room and smithy, to say nothing of food stores, are now replaced by a small tractor shed. Additional to such changes, we find

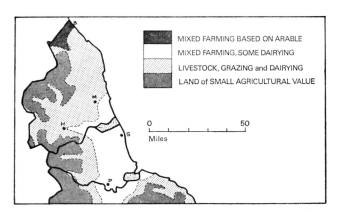

MIXED FARMING BASED ON ARABLE

MIXED FARMING, SOME DAIRYING

LIVESTOCK, GRAZING and DAIRYING

LAND of SMALL AGRICULTURAL VALUE

0                                    50

Miles

31    Types of farming in the North East. (Based on the *Land Utilisation Survey* of 1945. It may be contrasted with Fig 33)

regional variations of the very style of the buildings and their materials, resulting from climatic or geological conditions. Thus some farms are built of brick, with red pantile roofs, whereas others are of stone—ashlar, rubble or cobble—and roofs may be of flagstone or even (rarely now) of heather thatch. Again, the size of the average holding and the richness or poverty of the soil will control the size of farm layout. To take two extremes: in east Northumberland, large estate farms have extensive ranges of buildings, with terraces of farm-workers' cottages attached, whereas in Weardale one sees small scattered farmsteads each worked by a single family, with stable, byre and hay loft under a continuation of the house roof.

In general, the building requirements of a nineteenth-century farm were:

1   *House* for owner or foreman and perhaps additional housing for workers. Not infrequently the house is the oldest building on the farm, probably being the most substantial when first built, but having been modified over the years. In smaller farms an upstairs room or loft was used to house the unmarried hind and itinerant seasonal workers, often Irish.

On the large farms of east Northumberland one frequently sees a sizeable row of a dozen or so houses, giving some indication of the scale of labour required in the mid-nineteenth century. Occasionally, as at Beal near Holy Island, what amounts almost to a hamlet is to be seen. Here about twenty-five single-storey cottages were built round three sides of a square, with a stone wall separating their 'backyards' from the central open grassy area. The fourth side comprised a range of earth closets whose doors opened away from the square. This fine group, built to house estate workers, was vacated in 1964.

2   *Stables* for several horses, the number depending on the size of farm and amount of arable land. Additionally many farms had a small smithy where shoeing was done and equipment repaired. In some areas the village blacksmith visited the farm weekly to carry out this work.

3   *Livestock buildings.* Cattle required a byre where they could be milked and an adjoining building would house young stock and bullocks during the winter. A dairy to deal with milk, cheese and butter (where appropriate) was generally attached to the house.

A small piggery is often found, to take two sows in adjoining pens, sometimes with a stone chute built into the wall through which the swill would be poured. Other specialised buildings may sometimes be observed, as at Lowick, not far south of Berwick-on-Tweed, where hens seem to have been kept on a remarkably large scale in the late-eighteenth century. At that time Berwick was noted for its export of eggs and in 1797 more than 5,000 chests (each containing 1,600 eggs) were sent to London. At a current price of 7/6 per 100, this represented an annual trade of more than £30,000.[2] Shortly after the Napoleonic Wars this trade dwindled since London could be more readily supplied from Ireland and the Continent.

Dovecots were not an uncommon feature of farms. The free-standing medieval ones are now rather derelict; but small groups of openings are often built into eighteenth- and nineteenth-century buildings, presumably mostly for their decorative effect.

4   *Crop storage* buildings such as granaries, hay lofts and barns. The barn, to which the corn crop was brought from the field, was generally a high airy building, but the granary where the threshed grain was stored in sacks was generally at first-floor level to reduce rat-infestation and to keep the crop dry. Since grain can easily absorb strong odours, the granary was not built over the cowhouse or stable, but over the cart

shed or similar building. The hay loft, on the other hand, was frequently put above the byre or stable in order to simplify feeding.

5  *The cart-shed* might be, as mentioned above, an integral part of the granary, or it might be a separate single-storey building. The chief requirement was a wide open front for the entry of vehicles. Its depth varied according to the length of the carts or wagons typical of the area and its length according to the size of the farm.

6  *Miscellaneous buildings* for specialised functions such as threshing from the crop storage group of buildings. The first successful threshing machine was invented in Scotland by Andrew Meikle in 1788 and quickly spread south; it was a small structure fixed in the barn and powered by water, wind or horse. Very few remaining examples of water-powered threshers have been discovered in the North East (one for example near Blanchland) and none whatsoever of wind-powered ones, but several horse-turned threshers have been found, and their empty buildings are very common. These, known as wheel-houses, are described on page 188. By about 1850, horse-powered threshers were being replaced by steam power and the chimney often to be seen on Northumberland farms indicates where this machinery was once housed (p 190).

The recording of farm layouts as a research project has only begun in the last few years and it is therefore rather early to look at detailed results, yet the rapid changes now taking place in farming make such recording a matter of some urgency. During the eighteenth and nineteenth centuries, when a farmer desired to change his farming method he converted his existing buildings, or added another building, whereas nowadays grants are more readily available for new buildings, than for conversions. The old structures are therefore demolished to make way for the new. Most of our farms today show something of the history of that farm, and therefore of the farming of the region, over the past two if not three centuries. But the next few years will see much of this evidence destroyed without trace. If farming is accepted as an industry, here are industrial structures which are widely available for study and recording.

In one chapter it is not possible to describe, even briefly, the many variations of farm buildings to be found in a region so wide-ranging as the North East. Instead a few structures of particular relevance to, or typical of, this region have been selected.

## 'Green villages'

Villages represent the largest cluster of rural buildings and, whilst it may seem to be over-extending the reference of industrial archaeology to include them, mention must be made in the North East, of the so-called 'green villages' which are a particular feature of County Durham.[3] Here are to be seen upwards of fifty rectangular villages, mostly oriented east-west, with juxtaposed buildings surrounding an open green, making an enclosure with strictly limited ways of access. It is tempting to relate these to the needs of defence, and the many fortified towers and houses, particularly in Northumberland, make this seem feasible. But the origins of the 'green villages' are still obscure and may well be associated with agrarian needs, and certainly pre-date the period of Border turmoil. Heighington, Staindrop, Bishopton and Hurworth are good examples.

## THRESHING

### By horse power

The history of threshing is put properly into perspective when one realises that only for 180 years or so have we had mechanical threshing and for several thousand years before that the flail was used. Our forebears of the eighteenth century threshed by flail as did the Egyptians. The process of threshing is essentially that of separating the grain from the straw and from the chaff or small 'wrappers' which have protected the individual grains. The modern thresher differs relatively little from that designed by Andrew Meikle in 1788 and by a kind of rubbing movement the three components of the harvest are taken apart. The straw is then taken away by 'straw arms' or rollers with long projecting spikes which pick up the straw and allow the grain and chaff to fall on to a shaker. Through this perforated shaking-plate is sent a current of air which winnows or blows away the lighter chaff. The grain itself may be graded by quality according to the weight of the grain, by this same current of air.

We have seen (p 186) that, although Meikle's machine was capable of being operated by wind, water or horse power, it was the latter which was most commonly used, at any rate in the North East. It was clearly the most dependable method. Wind might not be available when needed and water required a large dam to maintain constant power, whereas horses were always on the farm. Indeed threshing would usually be a winter-time occupation when the horses might be without outdoor work.

To convert the pulling power of a horse to rotary motion necessitated the horse, or horses, walking in a circle, pulling around a kind of wooden roundabout. Such machinery had been in use for centuries and in the eighteenth century many factories were powered in this way, so adaptation was all that was required. Soon a simple design was arrived at and a single-storey building to house it became fairly standard practice. In general the diameter of the horse-wheel, as the machine was often called, was about 25ft, for to walk the horses in a smaller circle was less comfortable and therefore less efficient, whereas to make it larger was simply more expensive. Up to six horses might be harnessed into one wheel, but the average number was three. The wheel was mostly wooden, with a circular rack gear on top. This in turn meshed with a gear on the 'tumbling-shaft', a stout wooden shaft which ran horizontally from the wheelhouse through the wall into the barn, where it drove the thresher.[4]

Very few horse-wheels now survive. Part of one, from Framwellgate, near the city of Durham, is preserved by the Regional Open Air Museum and one still stands in position (though without the rack gear) at Great Ayton in Yorkshire. Another, now re-erected at the Regional Open Air Museum, came from Berwick Hill, in south Northumberland,[5] and a measured drawing of this is seen in Fig 32.

While the wheels are scarce, the buildings which once housed them are very common. In some areas almost every other farm still has its wheelhouse or 'gin-gang'. Most middle-aged farmers remember these machines in use and the speed with which they have been destroyed indicates what can happen to other machinery and struc-

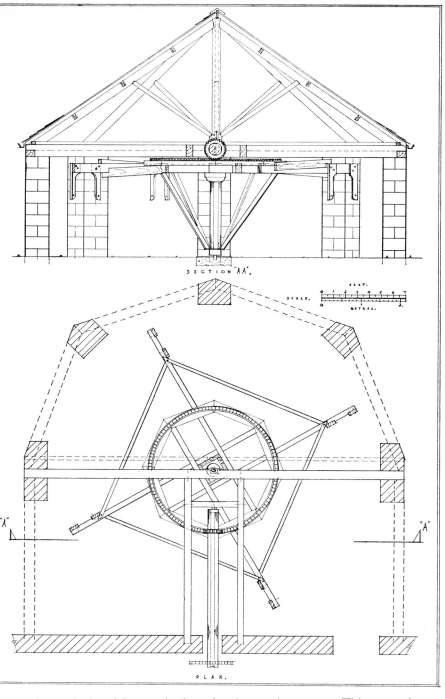

SECTION "AA".

SCALE.

FEET.

METRES.

PLAN.

"A"   "A"

32   An agricultural horse-wheel: early nineteenth century. This example
has been preserved at Beamish, the Regional Open Air Museum

tures. The wheelhouses, unlike the machines they held, can be put to many uses—cowsheds, tractor sheds, piggeries, hen houses—and have therefore outlived their original purpose. They can be recognised by their general shape, size and position, and internally the main cross beam will be seen still to have the bolt holes where the plummer block was fixed to support the upper end bearing of the central vertical pivot. From this beam two parallel beams (about 2ft apart) run to the adjoining barn wall and it was between these that the tumbling-shaft rotated.

It will be clear from the date of Meikle's work that wheelhouses on farms date from 1790 at the very earliest and most are of about 1800 to 1850. By the time of the Great Exhibition of 1851 an outdoor wheel had been designed which worked at ground level, the horses stepping over the metal driving shaft (the equivalent of the tumbling-shaft) as they walked. This much cheaper model sufficed for smaller farms and meanwhile an improvement had become available for larger farms—the steam engine. We may conclude that probably very few wheelhouses were put up after the middle of the nineteenth century.

*By stationary steam engine*

Although first invented in the early 1700s, and improved by Watt in the 1770s and 1780s, the steam engine remained a large and costly machine until the early years of the nineteenth century. By 1844, Henry Stephens in his *Book of the Farm* was able to illustrate a small vertical-cylinder steam engine which could be built into a barn. Loudon's *Encyclopaedia of Agriculture* of 1825 illustrates an 'ideal' farm with chimney, and one may deduce that some very advanced landowners were then just beginning to experiment with this new form of farm power. Probably by the middle of the century most well-to-do farmers were thinking of steam threshing and stationary steam engines continued to be installed until the late years of the century. By then, however, portable engines and mobile steam traction-engines were becoming commonplace, for a mobile engine which could be put to several uses had obvious advantages over a fixed one with limited applications.

As to dated examples in the North East, an engine built by Gilkes, Wilson & Co of Middlesbrough and dated 1852 on the cylinder base, has been taken in store from St Helen's Auckland for the Regional Open Air Museum. A brick chimney once serving a farm engine near Gilling West, Yorkshire, is dated 1874. Two other stationary engines have been discovered on north-eastern farms: one near Newbiggin-by-the-Sea, the other near Great Whittington. Part of the first is also in store for the Regional Open Air Museum, the latter is privately preserved at Peepy Farm, Riding Mill.

If the engines themselves are scarce, proof of their existence is simple to observe, for such engines required a substantial chimney and these are easily spotted. A rough survey (Fig 33) has produced 24 farm chimneys in Northumberland, 3 in Durham and 5 in Yorkshire, and no doubt several have been missed and others will have been felled:

*Northumberland*
> *Berwick-on-Tweed area:* Shoreswood Hall Farm, NT 958466; Shoreswood Farm, NT 941465; New East Farm, NT 978562; Mount Pleasant Farm, NT 954509; Buttery Hall Farm, NU 025447
> *Alnwick area:* Craster South Farm, NU 251194; Longbank Farm, NU 243143; Wood House Farm, NU 211083; Preston Farm, NU 186257; Ratcheugh Farm, NU 232147; Thrunton Farm, NU 089109
> *Amble area:* Hope House, NU 256031; Tugton East Farm, NU 268018; Hound Dene Farm, NU 244066; Thirston New Houses, NZ 181992; Chester House, NU 236025; Cavil Head, NU 230027
> *Morpeth area:* Shotton Farm, NZ 225780; Plessey New House Farm, NZ 239784
> *Corbridge area:* Shildonhill Farm, NZ 036669
> *Hexham area:* New Bingfield Farm, NY 985737; Chollerton Farm, NZ 932720; Fourstones Farm, NY 892680
> *Newbiggin-by-the-Sea area:* Manor Farm, Woodhorn, NZ 297889

*County Durham*
> Beamish Home Farm, Beamish, NZ 216543; High Flatts Farm, Chester-le-Street, NZ 262527 (demolished 1971); St Helens Auckland

Farm, St Helens Auckland, NZ 190268 (engine and boiler dismantled and stored for Regional Open Air Museum)

*Cleveland District of Yorkshire*
Cleasby Hall Farm, Cleasby, NZ 249131; Crabtree House Farm, Gilling West, NZ 167053; Gilling Grange Farm, Gilling West (chimney dated 1874); Ryehills Farm, Marske, NZ 624226; Newton Morrell Farm, Newton Morrell, NZ 239095

These chimneys show interesting variations in shape, construction and materials. Their distribution was controlled by at least two factors: the proximity of cheap coal and the suitability of the area for corn crops. Furthermore, since they were expensive to install, only the larger farms or estate owners were able to take advantage of this technological development. The distribution map of these chimneys can be used to make a further point. Mention was made earlier of the recent *Land Utilisation Survey of Northumberland* which describes almost the entire county as being given over to grazing or stock-rearing. Comparison of that map (Fig 31) with the distribution of steam-threshing (Fig 33) shows clearly how the pattern of farming has changed in the county.

Finally, a point of interest may be observed at Beamish, on the home farm of Beamish Hall, once owned by the Shafto family. Here a well-built stone wheelhouse was converted to other use and replaced by a steam engine for which the fine chimney still stands. Another example of such replacement can be seen at Fourstones.

## JOHN FOWLER

Stationary steam engines were eventually succeeded by portable steam engines and these in turn by traction engines and one man who played a great part in this development was John Fowler who is commemorated by a monument in South Park, Darlington. There can be few civil engineers so commemorated: a large, plain and somewhat ugly red-granite block is surmounted by a bronze model of his balance plough and bears the simple inscription 'John Fowler, C.E., 1856'. (C.E. has nothing to do with his religion, indeed he married a

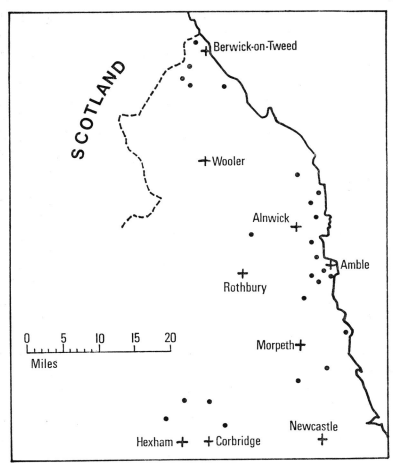

33  Farms with chimneys in Northumberland. Each dot represents
a farm with a chimney, indicating that here was once a stationary
steam-powered threshing machine (see Plate, p 144)

Quaker heiress, but is a not uncommon nineteenth-century way of
describing a civil engineer.)

John Fowler (1826–64) came to Teesside to study mechanical
engineering with Gilkes, Wilson, Hopkins & Co and eventually

M

married into the Pease family of Darlington. In 1849, visiting Ireland on behalf of his firm, he saw the poverty and distress of the potato famine and decided that food production there could be greatly helped by drainage. He set to work on this and at the Great Exhibition of 1851 he demonstrated a land-draining mole plough drawn by winch and horse-engine. Next he applied a steam engine to this work, by using drums mounted on spindles to propel the mole plough backwards and forwards across the field. When members of the Royal Agricultural Society saw this machinery at Lincoln in 1854 they saw the possibility of an economic method of mechanical cultivation and offered a prize of £200 to the machinery adjudged to be best.[6]

Fowler, still only 28, was dubious whether steam power could ever excel economically the use of horses on the land, but he regarded this offer as a personal challenge. His great difficulty was the unadaptability of the ordinary plough, but at length he fixed right- and left-handed shares to a see-saw frame and made a two-way plough. The Ipswich firm of Ransome & Simms made his first model and with this he managed to plough an acre in an hour. His demonstration in 1856 to the Royal Agricultural Society did not meet with entire success, for the assessors decided that horses would have been the cheaper by $2\frac{1}{2}$d per acre. Only a few weeks after his marriage, however, his machinery was demonstrated at Stirling where he gained an award of £200 from the Highland & Agricultural Society.

From this success he looked forward to the steam engine itself becoming mobile rather than merely portable and dragged by horses. He became joint founder of Messrs Hewitson & Fowler at Leeds, although he shortly afterwards lost his partner, and in 1863 the firm of John Fowler & Co began the production of steam traction-engines or road locomotives. A year later, having been advised to take fresh air and exercise, Fowler was thrown from his horse while hunting and died from tetanus following a fractured arm. The Darlington monument was erected after his death by the Pease family.

*Notes to this chapter are on p 202.*

# Notes and References to Volume One

CHAPTER ONE (*The North East.* P 13)

1 Several books have been drawn upon for this chapter, some more general than others. A. E. Smailes' *North England* is a valuable and readable historic geography and M. W. Flinn's *Men of Iron* gives a useful glimpse of the eighteenth-century operation of one industry. Two school books can be recommended for the reader who merely wants a superficial idea of the region: H. G. Bowling's *Land of the Three Rivers* and E. M. Coulthard's *From Tweed to Tees.*

2 *Men of Iron* quoted above should be read in conjunction with *The Law Book of the Crowley Ironworks*, also by Flinn. It is interesting to note that individuals and small groups of ironworkers continued in business in the area. The last of this long line of ironworkers, Mr Jack Hunter a chainsmith, retired in 1966 at the age of sixty-five. It is his equipment which has been preserved for incorporation in the Regional Open Air Museum.

3 Quoted by E. Hughes in the introduction to his *North Country Life in the Eighteenth Century.*

4 Armstrong was elected President of the British Association when that body paid its second visit to Newcastle in 1863 and this quotation comes from his presidential address.

5 From the publisher's preface to *Industrial Resources of Tyne, Tees and Wear*: Report of 1863 British Association's meetings in Newcastle.

6 W. Richardson, *History of the Parish of Wallsend*, 1923.

7 S. Middlebrook, *Newcastle upon Tyne, Its Growth and Achievements*, 1950.

8 *Victoria County History* for County Durham, vol 2.

9 This mention of an eighteenth-century steel furnace is a reference to Derwentcote, to be found under Hamsterley Colliery in the Durham Gazetteer.

10 The coal port mentioned here is Seaham Harbour; see Durham Gazetteer.

11 For a description of what has and is being done to preserve something of the history of the region, see Appendix 1.

12 This is, of course, a much simplified geological history of the region.

For more specific information reference should be made to the first few books listed in the Bibliography.

CHAPTER TWO (*Coal.* P 27)

1   Just as it may sometimes seem today that violence has to be shown before social injustices can be put right, so in the nineteenth century tragedies seemed necessary before working conditions were improved. Two great accidents in the Northern coalfield seem to make this point. The first was the Felling explosion in which ninety-two lives were lost. There had been earlier accidents of this nature, and there were to be others afterwards, but this particular one so impressed the Rev John Hodgson, Vicar of Felling, that he widely publicised it in a *Funeral Sermon*, published in 1813. As a direct result the Society for Preventing Accidents in Coal Mines was formed at Sunderland in the same year. John Buddle at once wrote giving a detailed account of the various systems employed in the ventilation of collieries, and this was published as the society's first Report in 1814. The society then approached Sir Humphrey Davy who expressed great interest and visited the area. By October 1815 he had constructed a safe lamp. By one of those coincidences, so frequently found in scientific discovery, George Stephenson produced a similar lamp almost simultaneously and both continued in use, side by side, for some years.

   A second terrible tragedy which directly resulted in improved conditions took place at New Hartley in Northumberland in 1862 (see Northumberland Gazetteer).

2   Matthias Dunn, *Winning and Working Collieries*, 1848.

3   Charles Tomlinson, *Cyclopaedia of Useful Arts and Manufactures*, 1857.

4   More information on this subject, specific to the Northumberland and Durham coalfield, will be found in the author's book: *The Great Northern Coalfield 1700–1900*, 1968.

5   Happily this valuable pamphlet, first published in 1708 and republished in 1845 and which has for long been virtually unobtainable, has been re-issued as a reprint (Newcastle, 1968).

6   John Holland, *Fossil Fuel*, 1835.

7   See note 1 above.

8   T. H. Hair, *Views of the Collieries of Northumberland and Durham*, 1844, reprinted 1969.

9   A description of various types of gins and whims is to be found in a paper by the author: 'The Horse as a Source of Rotary Power', in the

*Transactions* Newcomen Society, vol 33, 1962, 31–55. Coal-mining gins and whims are described and illustrated in his *The Great Northern Coalfield, 1700–1900*.

10  See the paper by G. M. Watkins, 'Vertical Winding Engines of Durham', *Transactions* Newcomen Society, vol 29, 205–10.

11  I am indebted to H. A. Townley for this observation.

12  An early example of a 'black wagon' is illustrated in Gabriel Jars' book *Voyages Métallurgiques* (1774 and 1781).

13  A man rode down alongside the coal-truck on the swinging platform, in order to free the bottom door of the truck. It is interesting to note that this typical feature of the north-eastern coal-truck (bottom-tipping) has persisted over more than two centuries.

14  Acknowledgement should be made here to the excellent book by R. A. Mott: *The History of Coke-Making*, 1936.

15  I am greatly indebted to Mr M. J. Edington for help with this section.

16  By way of comparison and contrast with the Durham pitman's home, is a short article by the writer, describing a late-nineteenth-century miner's cottage from the West Yorkshire coalfield: 'Yorkshire Miners' Cottages', *Folk Life*, 3, 1965, 92–6.

CHAPTER THREE (*Lead*. P 57)

1  I am indebted to Dr Mark Hughes for this observation.

2  Westgarth Forster, *Treatise on a Section of the Strata . . .*, 1821.

3  Much useful information on this area is given by L. C. Coombes: 'Lead Mining in East and West Allendale', *Archaeologia Aeliana*, 36, 1958, 245–70.

4  Paul N. Wilson, 'The Nent Force Level', *Transactions* Cumberland & Westmorland Antiquarian & Archaeological Society, 63, 1963, 253–80.

5  *Ure's Dictionary of Arts Manufactures and Mines*, edited by R. Hunt (7th ed), vol 2, 1878, Fig 660.

6  As for note 2 above.

7  *Ure's Dictionary* (note 5 above) is particularly useful in this respect, as also is J. Percy: *Metallurgy* (four volumes, 1861–80), and Spon's *Dictionary of Engineering*, 1874.

8  Partly based upon A. Raistrick, 1936 (see Bibliography) and partly upon Westgarth Forster (1821).

9  Useful illustrations and text are to be found in *Ure's Dictionary*.

10  Two copies exist of James Mulcaster's manuscript 'An Account of the Method of Smelting Lead Ore . . . in the Northern Part of England'.

One is in Newcastle, as stated in the text, the other (believed to be a later copy—perhaps of 1806—having certain additions), is in the Central Reference Library, Wigan, Lancs. The Newcastle document is fully transcribed in the *Bulletin* Historical Metallurgy Group, 2, 1971, 45–62.

CHAPTER FOUR (*Iron and Steel*. P 81)

1  These engines, and indeed the whole works, were well recorded by the Teesside Industrial Archaeology Group. Fig 16 which was first reproduced in *Bulletin* no 6 of the North East Industrial Archaeology Society (1968), is here reproduced by kind permission of Mr J. K. Harrison. It was measured and drawn by him and his pupils at Eston Grammar School in 1967.

2  Useful sources for further information are the several memoirs of the Geological Survey and A. E. Smailes, *North England*, 1960.

3  Very useful summaries are given by I. L. Bell, 1863 and 1864 and by H. Louis, 1916 (see Bibliography).

4  See the Bibliography for sources by J. Bewick (1861), S. K. Chapman (1967) and T. E. Rounthwaite (1957).

5  See H. R. Schubert, *History of the British Iron and Steel Industry*, 1957.

6  Two books which help one to understand the variety of skills of the blacksmith are: J. A. R. Stevenson, *The Din of a Smithy*, 1932; and Garry Hogg, *Hammer and Tongs*, 1964.

7  This Romaldkirk example of a tyre-bender has recently been rescued for use in the Regional Open Air Museum.

8  For a more detailed analysis of the remarkable business administration of Ambrose Crowley see M. W. Flinn, 'The Law Book of the Crowley Ironworks', *Surtees Society*, vol 167, 1957.

9  *The Northern Tribune* (*A Periodical for the People*), Newcastle, 1854, vol 1, 27.

CHAPTER FIVE (*Other Minerals*. P 97)

1  A. Raistrick, 'The Copper Deposits of Middleton Tyas', *The Naturalist*, May 1936, 111–15.

2  Gabriel Jars, *Voyages Métallurgiques*, 1774 and 1781, Lyons and Paris.

3  F. Brook, 'Fallowfield Lead and Witherite Mines', *Journal Industrial Archaeology*, 4 no 4, 1967, 311–22.

4  W. Gray, *Chorographia*, 1649.

5   Information kindly supplied by Messrs Jas H. Harrison Ltd, Spring-well Quarries, Gateshead.

6   W. J. Cudworth, *Darlington Half Holiday Guide*, 1899.

7   The following papers add up to what is so far known of this isolated little works:

Frank Atkinson, 'A Pencil Mill at Cronkley Scar', North East Industrial Archaeology Society *Bulletin*, 5, 1968, 17–18.

Alan Stoyel, 'The Cronkley Pencil Mill', North East Industrial Archaeology Society *Bulletin*, 7, 1968, 2–4.

Vera Chapman, 'Slate Pencil Mill', North East Industrial Archaeology Society *Bulletin*, 8, 1969, 3–16.

H. L. Beadle, 'Cronkley and Newbiggin Pencil Mills', North East Industrial Archaeology Society *Bulletin*, 9, 1969, 21–5.

8   For example: 'A Letter with Respect to a Reverberatory Draw-kiln for burning Lime', *Select Transactions of the Society of Improvers in the Knowledge of Agriculture in Scotland*, Edinburgh, 1743, 190–5.

9   William Marshall, *Rural Economy of Yorkshire*, 1788, 1, 338.

10  From information kindly supplied by the manager of the Throckley, Northumberland, brickworks.

11  Recent excavations on pottery spoil heaps by the Sunderland Industrial Archaeology Group and Sunderland Museum are helping to identify the products of various potteries on Wearside.

12  *Pottery Gazette & Glass Trade Review*, June 1952.

13  H. C. Darby, *Historical Geography*, 1951, 226.

14  Sir William Brereton, 'Journey through Durham and Northumberland', in M. A. Richardson's *Reprints of Rare Tracts of Northern Counties*, 1847–9.

15  Lord Harley, 'Journeys in England, 1725', Historical MSS Commission's Report on MSS of Duke of Portland, 6, 105.

16  Another interesting 'account of the cost . . . of building 6 new pans' of 1726, is printed in John Wallace's *History of Blyth*, 1869, 149ff.

17  R. A. Foster, *The Industrial Development of Seaton Sluice*, 1948. Unpublished thesis in Newcastle Central Library, no 97909.

CHAPTER SIX (*Transport*. P 117)

1   The general historical background to the Tyne—for so long the centre of the North East—is based on a variety of books and pamphlets ranging from John Brand's *History and Antiquities of Newcastle* (1789), by way of the several British Association Reports 1863, 1889, 1915, 1949, and Tyne Improvement Commissioner's Reports, up to

a fine summary of the recent position by A. S. Travis 1965 in connection with the Tyne Landscape Survey.

2 J. Fuller, *History of Berwick Upon Tweed*, 1799. See further reference to the export of eggs under Livestock buildings, Chapter Nine, p 185.

3 See note 17 for Chapter Five.

4 *Victoria County History* for County Durham, vol 2.

5 Very little has been written about this small but interesting industrial harbour. A note of its development is to be found in the paper by S. K. Chapman, 'Port Mulgrave Ironstone Workings', *North East Industrial Archaeology Society Bulletin*, 5, 1968, 3–7.

6 There were three Acts of 1767 for the area:

(a) that for the Ure and Ripon Canal. Under this the Ure was made navigable from Swale Nab past Boroughbridge to Ox Close, and the Ripon Canal thence to Ripon: it was opened throughout in late 1772.

(b) that for the Ouse from Widdington Ings to Swale Nab, including Linton Lock, together with the Swale to Morton Bridge, and the Bedale Beck to Bedale. Under this Linton Lock was completed and opened in August 1769 and the Ouse section completed. On the Swale a lock was completed at Topcliffe Mill in January 1769, and some other work done, including the building of a towpath to Wiske mouth; there is no record of a commercial craft reaching Morton Bridge. The same is true of Bedale Beck—Leeming Lock was built, another one above it began, and work done at Bedale itself, but there is no record of its ever being used.

Linton Lock itself was in bad state from about 1783 to about 1788, and traffic was certainly hindered during the period.

(c) the Codbeck to Thirsk. Work was done at Thirsk and a lock built at Sowerby. The navigation was, however, never finished, though two 40 ton craft did reach Thirsk in 1770—probably the only ones. I am indebted to Kenneth Hoole for this note.

7 I am indebted to Alan Voce for help in tracing the history of this little-used stretch of canal. Between 1767 and 1778 several assignments of proportions of tolls along the navigation were made (Pease Papers at the North Riding County Record Office, Northallerton). The minutes of the Ouse Commissioners (York Library) contain references to the navigation. I must also thank Michael Wyatt Wheeler for ascertaining the dimensions of Linton Lock and checking other data. My thanks also go to a WEA class who helped in the survey of the Leeming Lock and the Bedale Basin.

8   Fig 25 and some information about the Mandale and Portrack Cuts is based on M. Heavisides' pamphlet *Rambles by the River Tees*, 1921.

9   A useful section on the development of the toll roads in County Durham is given in J. Bailey's *Agriculture of County Durham*, 1810. An interesting text and several fine maps, etc for the region are to be found in the recent Archive Teaching Unit No 2 *Travel in the Turnpike Age*, prepared by D. R. Brenchley and C. Shrimpton and published by the University of Newcastle, 1968.

10  Further details are to be found in a booklet issued by the then County Borough of Middlesbrough, to celebrate the Transporter Bridge Jubilee in 1961.

11  This vast and complex subject clearly cannot be synthesised into a chapter, yet mention is essential. As stated in the text, an attempt has been made to sketch some of the more significant events leading to the evolution of the North Eastern Railway system, and particularly to highlight some of the (perhaps lesser-known) early features which can still be observed in the landscape.

It has not seemed either necessary or desirable to quote references in this section, as so many authoritative works are readily available. A selection of titles will be found in the Bibliography.

12  Although the rail route east of Medomsley amounted to some 24 miles, the distance covered is only 18 miles; the extra mileage involved having resulted from the route which the line had to take due to the difficulty of the terrain. I am indebted to Kenneth Hoole for this observation.

13  This bridge has recently been demolished, but the metal plate bearing the inscription has been preserved by the local council.

CHAPTER SEVEN (*Power*. P 150)

1   See also the author's paper 'The Horse as a Source of Rotary Power', *Transactions* Newcomen Society, 33, 1962, 31–55.

2   I am indebted to Mr T. Hay for this observation.

3   This is a confusing place! The Post Office uses DALTON, the road sign states COLD HESLEDON, the Ordnance Survey prefers NEW HESLEDON and Bartholomew's *Gazetteer of the British Isles* offers only COLDHESLEDON.

4   See R. H. Parsons, *Early Days of the Power Station Industry*, 1939.

CHAPTER EIGHT (*Manufacturing*. P 158)

1   M. W. Flinn, *Men of Iron*, 1962.

N

2   D. Dougan, *History of North East Shipbuilding*, 1968.
3   A booklet was issued on the occasion of the opening of 'Turbinia Hall' at the Museum of Science & Engineering, September, 1961.
4   A leaflet is issued by South Shields Public Library.
5   L. T. C. Rolt, *Thomas Newcomen*, 1963.
6   *Sykes' Local Records*, 1, 242, 251; and *Transactions* North East Institute of Mining, 15, 209.
7   Muirhead's *Life of Watt*, 274. Watt remarked that it went sluggishly and irregularly, having no flywheel.
8   W. A. Campbell, et al, *The Old Tyneside Chemical Trade*, 1964.
9   Francis Buckley, 'Glasshouses on the Tyne in the 18th century', *Journal* Society of Glass Technology, 10, 1926, 26–52.
10  A short but interesting article which illustrates the Newcastle, Bristol and Chester towers (by G. Price) is: 'Shot Towers' *Northern Architect*, 10, 1963, 222–3.
11  A description of the Newcastle shot tower and its method of operation by Ian Glendenning: 'Shot Making and the Shot Tower at Elswick', *Proceedings* Society of Antiquaries of Newcastle upon Tyne (5th series), 1, 1955, 351–62.
12  T. Fordyce, *History of the County Palatine of Durham*, vol 2, 83.
13  *The Story of Associated Lead*, issued by the manufacturers of that name, 1949.
14  Stuart Smith, 'Wire-Rope Making at Sunderland', North East Industrial Archaeology Society *Bulletin*, 7, 1968, 8–9.

CHAPTER NINE (*Agriculture*. P 183)

1   *Victoria County History* for County Durham.
2   J. Fuller, *History of Berwick Upon Tweed*, 1799.
3   H. Thorpe, 'The Green Villages of Co. Durham', *Transactions* Institute of British Geographers, 15, 1949, 155–80.
4   Frank Atkinson, 'The Horse as a Source of Rotary Power', *Transactions* Newcomen Society, 33, 1962, 31–55.
5   This 'wheel' has been reconstructed with an existing wheelhouse at Beamish Home Farm, as shown in Fig 32.
6   *Dictionary of National Biography*.

# Bibliography

CHAPTER ONE (*The North East*. P 13)
*Geology*
Eastwood, T. *Regional Geology*; *Northern England*, 1946
Kendall, P. F., and Wroot, H. *Geology of Yorkshire*, 1924
Smailes, A. E. *North England*, 1960
Stamp, L. D. *Britain's Structure and Scenery*, 1946
Wilson, V. *Regional Geology: East Yorkshire*, 1948

*General Topography and History*
Bowling, H. G. *et al. Land of the Three Rivers*, 1958
British Association. *Scientific Survey of North Eastern England*, 1949
Coulthard, E. M. *From Tweed to Tees*, 1934
Daysh, G. H.J. *Survey of Industrial Facilities of the North East Coast*, 1936
Jars, Gabriel. *Voyages Métallurgiques*, 1774 and 1781, Lyons and Paris
Mess, H. A. *Industrial Tyneside: A Social Survey*, 1928
Museum of Science & Engineering, Newcastle. *Catalogue*, 1960
North East Development Council. *Three Rivers Heritage*, 1964
Pevsner, N. *Buildings of England: County Durham*, 1953
Pevsner, N. *Buildings of England: Northumberland*, 1957
Rowe, D. J. 'The Economy of the North-East in the Nineteenth Century:
    A Survey' (with bibliography), *Northern History*, 6, 1971, 117–47
Tomlinson, Charles. *Cyclopaedia of Useful Arts*, 1857

*Counties and Areas*
Backhouse, J. *Upper Teesdale, Past and Present*, 1896
Boyle, J. R. *Guide to the County of Durham*, 1892
Eden, Sir T. *Durham*, 1952
Gibson, W. S. *Historical Memoir on Northumberland*, 1862
Harland, O. *Yorkshire North Riding*, 1951
Heavisides, M. *Rambles in Cleveland*, 1901
Hodgkin, J. E. *Durham*, 1913
Kelly. *Directory of Durham*, 1914
McCord, N. *Durham History from the Air*, 1971
Mitton, G. E. *County of Durham*, 1924

*Shell Guide to Durham and Northumberland*
Surtees, R. *History of Durham*, 1816–40
Taylor, H. A. (compiler). *Northumberland History: Guide to records in Newcastle*, 1963
Tomlinson, W. W. *Guide to Northumberland*, 1889
Victoria County History. *County of Durham*, 1907
Wallis, J. *Natural History and Antiquities of Northumberland and Durham*, 1769
Wardell, J. W. *Economic History of Teesside*, 1960
Wright, A. *Cleveland*, 1966

*Towns*
Allsopp, B. (ed). *Historic Architecture of Newcastle*, 1967
Andrews, W. *Bygone Durham*, 1898
Anon. *Historic and Descriptive View of Durham*, 1847
Barber, B. 'The Concept of the Railway Town and the Growth of Darlington 1801–1911', *Transport History*, 3, 1970, 283–92
*Berwick-upon-Tweed Guide*, 1937
*Bishop Auckland and District: An Illustrated Account*, 1900
Bourne, H. *History of Newcastle upon Tyne*, 1736
Bowling, H. G. (ed). *Some Chapters on the History of Sunderland*, 1969
Brand, J. *History and Antiquities of Newcastle*, 1789
Britton, J., and Brayley, E. W. *Description of Durham*, 1810
Crawford, T. *Notes on Nineteenth Century Walker*, 1904
Cudworth, W. J. (ed). *Darlington Half Holiday Guide*, 1899
*Darlington Corporation Handbook.* 1927
Dodd, J. J. *History of Spennymoor*, 1897
Forster, R. *History of Corbridge*, 1881
Fuller, J. *History of Berwick upon Tweed*, 1799
Heavisides, M. *History of Stockton-on-Tees*, 1917
Longstaffe, D. *History and Antiquities of Darlington*
Mackenzie, E. *History of Newcastle and Gateshead*, 1827
Middlebrook, S. *Newcastle upon Tyne, its Growth and Achievements*, 1950
Pike, R. (pub). *Descriptive Account of Bishop Auckland, Barnard Castle and Spennymoor*
Richardson, W. *History of the Parish of Wallsend*, 1923
Sunderland, N. *History of Darlington*, 1967
Tate, G. *History of Alnwick*, 1866
Wallace, J. *History of Blyth*, 1869
Wardell, J. W. *History of Yarm*, 1957

Wooler, E., and Boyde, A. C. *Historic Darlington*, 1913
Wright, A. B. *History of Hexham*, 1823

*Social History*
Armstrong, W. H. (compiler). *Book of Songs by Thomas Armstrong*, 1930
Hughes, E. *North Country Life in the Eighteenth Century*, 1952
MacDermott, T. P. *Centuries of Conflict*, 1965
Miller, E. (compiler). *Eyewitness 1: Industrial Revolution in the North East*, 1967
Miller, E. (compiler). *Eyewitness 2: The North East in the Early Nineteenth Century*, 1968
Pybus, R. 'Writing: North East', *Stand*, 8, no 2, 1966, 11–23
Readshaw, T. *History of the Bishop Auckland Industrial Co-operative Society*, 1910
Smith, H. J. *Report to Board of Health on Darlington, 1850*, 1967

CHAPTER TWO (*Coal.* P 27)
Akenhead, D. (pub). *Picture of Newcastle upon Tyne . . . and Description of the Coal Mines*, 1807
Ashton, T. S., and Sykes, J. *Coal Industry of the Eighteenth Century*, 1929
Atkinson, Frank. *The Great Northern Coalfield 1700–1900*, 1968
Atkinson, P. 'The Isabella Winding Engine, Hetton-le-Hole', *Journal Stephenson Engineering Society*, vol for 1955–6, 75–97
Bell, J. T. W. *Plans of the Great Northern Coalfield*, 1843–61
Boyd, R. N. *Coal Pits and Pitmen*, 1892
C., J. *The Compleat Collier*, 1708, reprinted 1968
Dunn, Matthias. *Winning and Working Collieries*, 1848
Fleming, K. 'Chaldron Wagons at Seaham Harbour', *Industrial Railway Record*, no 10, June 1966, 236–7
Free, J. 'The Warden Law Haulage Engine, Hetton-le-Hole', *Journal Stephenson Engineering Society*, vol for 1955–6, 98–118
Galloway, R. L. *Annals of Coal Mining and the Coal Trade*, 1898
Gibson J. *Plan of the Collieries of the River Tyne and Wear*, 1787
Greenwell, G. C. *Glossary of the Terms used in the Coal Trade of Northumberland and Durham*, 1888
Hair, T. H. *Views of the Collieries in Northumberland and Durham*, 1844, reprinted 1969
Holland, J. *Fossil Fuel*, 1835
Lee, C. E. 'The Wagonways of Tyneside', *Archaeologia Aeliana* (4th series), 29, 1951, 135–202

Mott, R. A. *The history of Coke-making*, 1936
Mountford, C. E., and Charlton, L. G. 'Lintz: a colliery line', *Industrial Railway Record*, no 15, September 1967, 95–9
Nef, J. U. *Rise of the British Coal Industry*, 1932
Rogers, E. 'On the Manufacture of Charcoal and Coke', *Proceedings* Institution Mechanical Engineers, vol for 1857, 25–40
Steavenson, A. L. 'The Manufacture of Coke in the Newcastle and Durham Districts', *Transactions* North East Institute Mining Engineers, 8, 1860, 109–35
Turnbull, L., and Tyson, J. C. 'Coals from Newcastle', *Archive Teaching Unit no 1*, 1968
Watkins, G. M. 'Vertical Winding Engines of Durham', *Transactions* Newcomen Society, 29, 1955, 205–19

CHAPTER THREE (*Lead*. P 57)
Anon. *The Story of Associated Lead*, c1949
Beadle, H. L. 'Lead Smelting Mills of Teesdale', Durham County Local History Society *Bulletin*, 11, 1969, 2–10
Brook, F. 'Fallowfield Lead and Witherite Mines', *Journal Industrial Archaeology*, 4, no 4, 1967, 311–22
Clough, R. T. *Lead Smelting Mills of the Yorkshire Dales*, 1962
Coombes, L. C. 'Lead Mining in East and West Allendale', *Archaeologia Aeliana* (4th series), 36, 1958, 245–70
Dunham, K. C. *Geology of the Northern Pennine Orefield*, 1948
Forster, Westgarth. *Treatise on a section of the Strata . . .*, 1821
Foster-Smith, J. R. 'A Glossary of technical terms used in the North Pennine Metalliferous Mining Fields', *Transactions* Northern Cavern & Mine Research Society, 1, no 2, 1964, 5–21
Hunt, C. J. *The Lead Mines of the Northern Pennines*, 1970
Monkhouse, J. 'Smelt Mill at Langley, Northumberland: 1768–80', *Transactions* Institute of Mining & Metallurgy, 49, 1940, 701–9
Mulcaster, James. 'An Account of the Method of Smelting Lead Ore . . . in the Northern Part of England' (c1795), transcribed in the *Bulletin* of the Historical Metallurgy Group, 5, no 2, 1971, 45–62
Pattinson, H. L. 'Smelting lead ore and refining lead in Northumberland, Cumberland and Durham', *Transactions* Natural History Society Northumberland & Durham, 2, 1831, 152–77
Percy, J. 'Lead', *Metallurgy*, vol 3, 1870
Raistrick, A. 'Lead Mining and Smelting in West Yorkshire', *Transactions* Newcomen Society, 7, 1927, 81–96

Raistrick, A. 'Lead Smelting in the North Pennines in the Seventeenth and Eighteenth Centuries', *Proceedings* University of Durham Philosophical Society, 9, 1936, 164–79

Raistrick, A. 'Ore-hearth Lead Smelting in the Seventeenth and Eighteenth Centuries', *Proceedings* University of Durham Philsophical Society, 10, 1950, 529–40

Raistrick, A. *Mines and Miners of Swaledale*, 1955

Raistrick, A. 'Lead Mining in West Yorkshire', *Journal* Leeds University Mining Society, 37, 1961, 59–64

Raistrick, A., and Jennings, B. *History of Lead Mining in the Pennines*, 1965

Sopwith, T. *Account of the Mining Districts of Alston Moor*, 1833

Walton, J. H. *Times Past in Upper Weardale*, c1960

Wilson, P. 'The Nent Force Level', *Transactions* Cumberland & Westmorland Antiquarian & Archaeological Society, 63 (new series), 1963, 253–80

CHAPTER FOUR (*Iron and Steel*. P 81)

Anderson, W. 'Ironstones in North East England', *North East Coast: Survey of Industrial Facilities*, 1949, chapter 3, 34–7

Bell, I. L. 'Manufacture of Iron in Connection with the Northumberland and Durham Coalfield', *Report to the British Association for 1863*, 730–64

Bell, I. L. 'The Manufacture of Iron . . .', *Transactions* North of England Institute of Mining Engineers, 13, 1864, 109–55

Bewick, J. *Geological Treatise on the District of Cleveland and Observations on Ironstone Mining*, 1861

Chapman, S. K. *Gazetteer of Cleveland Ironstone Mines*, 1967

Consett Iron Company. *Leaves from Consett Iron Company Letter Books*, 1962

Flinn, M. W. 'The Law Book of the Crowley Ironworks', *Surtees Society*, vol 167, 1957

Flinn, M. W. *Men of Iron*, 1962

Hayes, R. H., and Rutter, J. G. 'Rosedale Mines and Railway', *Transactions* Scarborough Archaeological Society, 2, no 11, 1968

Louis, H. 'The Iron and Steel Industry of Northumberland and Durham', *British Association Handbook to Newcastle*, 1916, 45–7

Raistrick, A. (ed). *North York Moors: National Park Guide*, 1966

Rounthwaite, T. E. 'The Rosedale Branch', *The Railway Observer*, 27 (January 1957, 5–7; February 1957, 32–3; March 1957, 60–2; April 1957, 92–4)

Schubert, H. R. *History of the British Iron and Steel Industry*, 1957
Tylecote, R. F. 'Mediaeval iron-smelting in Weardale', *Journal* Iron &
Steel Institute, 192, 1959, 26–34
Tylecote, R. F. 'Mediaeval Bloomeries in the North of England', *Vita Pro
Ferro* (Festschrift für Robert Durer), Schaffhausen, 1965

CHAPTER FIVE (*Other Minerals*. P 97)
Beadle, H. L. 'Carr Crags Quarry', North East Industrial Archaeological
Society *Bulletin*, 8, 1969, 24–8
Chapman, Vera. 'Slate Pencil Mill in Upper Teesdale', North East
Industrial Archaeological Society *Bulletin*, 8, 1969, 3–16
Fowler, A. 'Salt, Anhydrite and Gypsum in North East England', *North
East Coast: Survey of Industrial Facilities*, 1949, chapter 6
Raistrick, A. 'The Copper Deposits of Middleton Tyas', *The Naturalist*,
May 1936, 111–15
Stoyel, A. J. 'The Cronkley Pencil Mill', North East Industrial Archaeo-
logical Society *Bulletin*, 7, 1968, 2–4
Wailes, R. 'Water-driven Mills for Grinding Stone', *Transactions* New-
comen Society, 39, 1970, 95–119

CHAPTER SIX (*Transport*. P 117)
Allen, C. J. *The North Eastern Railway*, 1964
Anon. *Weardale Railway Centenary 1847–1947*
Brenchley, D. R., and Shrimpton, C. 'Travel in the Turnpike Age'.
*University of Newcastle: Archive Teaching Unit no 2*, 1968
Cassie, W. Fisher. 'Early Civil Engineering in Northumbria', *Bulletin 43*,
University of Newcastle upon Tyne Dept of Civil Engineering, 1972
Dodds, M. H. *The North Shields Lighthouses*, 1928
Gard, R. M., and Hartley, J. R. 'Railway in the Making', *University of
Newcastle: Archive Teaching Unit no 3*, 1969
Gard, R. M. (ed). *Northumberland Railways from 1700*, Exhibition Cata-
logue, 1969
Graham, F. *Views on the Newcastle and Carlisle Railway*, 1969
Heavisides, M. *Rambles by the River Tees*, 1921
Hoole, K. *North East England*, vol 4 of *Regional History of the Railways of
Great Britain*, 1965
Hoole, K. *Railways in Cleveland*, 1971
Humpidge, C. T. *et al*. 'Trams: Ten Years of Progress', *Tramway Museum
Society*, no 21, 1966
Jervoise, E. *Ancient Bridges of the North of England*, 1931

Lee, C. E. 'The Wagonways of Tyneside', *Archaeologia Aeliana*, 29, 1951, 135–202
Lee, C. E. 'Some Railway Facts and Fallacies', *Transactions* Newcomen Society, 33, 1962, 1–16
Lewis, M. J. T. *Early Wooden Railways*, 1970
Mountford, C. E. *The Bowes Railway*, 1966
Richardson, T. *History of the Darlington and Barnard Castle Railway*, 1877
Rolt, L. T. C. *George and Robert Stephenson*, 1960
Rounthwaite, T. E. 'The Railways of Weardale', *Railway Correspondence & Travel Society*, 1965
Tomlinson, W. W. *The North Eastern Railway*, 1914 (reprinted 1967)
Wilson, F. E. *The British Tram*, 1963

CHAPTER SEVEN (*Power*. P 150)
Atkinson, Frank. 'The Horse as a Source of Rotary Power', *Transactions* Newcomen Society, 33, 1962, 31–55
Linsley, S. M. *Ryhope Pumping Station*, 1973
Major, K. 'Windmills of Northumberland and Durham', *Journal Industrial Archaeology*, 4, no 4, 1967, 331–9
Parsons, R. H. *Early Days of the Power Station Industry*, 1939
Rolt, L. T. C. *Thomas Newcomen*, 1963
Wyatt-Wheeler, Michael. 'Waterworks Beam Engine', North East Industrial Archaeological Society *Bulletin*, 6, 1968, 16

CHAPTER EIGHT (*Manufacturing*. P 158)
Buckley, F. 'Glasshouses on the Tyne in the Eighteenth Century', *Transactions* Society Glass Technology, vol 10, 1926
Campbell, W. A. *Century of Chemistry on Tyneside*, 1968
Campbell, W. A. et al. *The Old Tyneside Chemical Trade*, 1964
Cochrane, A. *Early History of Elswick Works*, 1909
Dougan, D. *History of North East Shipbuilding*, 1968
Maidwell, C. F. *A Short History of Paper-Making in the North East*, 1959

CHAPTER NINE (*Agriculture*. P 183)
Bailey, J. *Agriculture of County Durham*, 1810
Bailey, J., and Culley, G. *Agriculture of Northumberland*, 1797
Beavis, H. et al. 'A Ginwheel in South East Northumberland', North East Industrial Archaeological Society *Bulletin*, 14, 1971, 13–19
Daysh, G. H. J., and Stamp, L. D. *Land of Britain: Northumberland* (Land Utilisation Survey), 1945

# Index

Reference should also be made to the Gazetteer (for place-names) and to the appropriate Appendices in Volume Two. References to illustrations are printed in italics.